FOURTH & TRENCHES

FOURTH & TRENCHES

by Chris Johnson

Library of Congress

ISBN-13: 978-0-5782066-8-4

First Printing July 2018
Printed in the United States

Cover Design by Bravo

www.4thandtrenches.com

10 9 8 7 6 5 4 3 2 1

Dedication

This book is dedicated to my family, my son, my mom, my big brothers, Stephen and Zach, and most importantly, to my baby brother, Tony.

Acknowledgements

I want to thank God before everything. My lil' brother, Tony, my son, my mom and all of my family and friends who supported Tony, and all of us through this storm.

To Judge Nancy Russo for understanding and believing in me. My P.O., Ms. Chyvonne Kimbrough, for being so real.

My Auntie Shondra for all the help, work and extra time she put in helping me through the entire process. In addition, thank you so much, Christopher Peterson, Channel 12News, Coach Rick, Coach Brown, John McDonald, and our city, East Cleveland.

FOURTH AND INCHES IS A FOOTBALL TERM THAT
MEANING YOU'RE INCHES AWAY FROM A NEW
SET OF DOWNS OR A TOUCHDOWN.

TRENCHES MEANS JUST WHAT IT IMPLIES...

Some names were changed to protect those who have been deemed guilty . . .

I'm Chris Johnson. I wrote this book. It's all from my perspective.

Hope you enjoy...

Chapter One

Tony couldn't wait to see his brothers' reaction after what they were about to experience.

Tony boarded the white shiny private jet with his agent and his three older brothers, Mell, Max and Stew followed.

"We're going to Dubai for the weekend," his other brother, Frank said into his cell phone, a slight grin on his face, he caught Tony's eye and nodded at him. "I'll call you when we get back to Cleveland." He hung up his phone and followed his brothers onto the jet.

None of Tony's brothers had ever been on a private jet before, and they were astounded by what they saw as they boarded the elegant flight. The marble interior, granite tabletops with champagne bottles on ice, velvet seats, smart TVs and the Brazilian hourglass-shaped flight attendant with her cleavage exposed had them at a loss for words.

Ten minutes after they boarded the flight the jet took off. Everyone kept their seats when the Captain turned the seatbelt sign off except Max. He roamed around the jet astonished, looking around from ceiling to floor like a kid in a candy store.

"Good evening gentlemen," the sexy flight attendant said with her Brazilian accent as she walked up the aisle. "Would you like an appetizer or beverage?"

Frank replied, "Yeah, let me get a double of D'ussé on the rocks and get Tony a Voss water."

"Damn nigga, he know how to talk, he can order his own drink," Stew said with obvious agitation.

"Get him a double, too, he need it as you can see," Frank said impassively as he nodded towards Stew.

Tony and his agent laughed and shook their heads.

"Aye, what's this button for?" Max asked as he hit a switch on the emergency panel on the wall.

Everyone turned, looked at Max and screamed "NOOOO! Don't touch tha-"

A loud siren went off...

Beep! Beep! Beep! The loud alarm clock and the smell of sizzling bacon woke Tony up from a deep sleep. He sat straight up and swiped his hand across his face. Looking confused, he jerked his head from side to side, his eyes darting around the room.

"Tony! You alright lil' bra?" Frank said. Frank had been brushing his hair and staring out their bedroom window into the ghetto streets of East Cleveland.

East Cleveland, the only city they'd ever lived in, at one time had been the home of the Rockefellers, the suburb where black people moved to move up in the world. Over time, the city fell apart. Now it was filled with crack heads, drug dealers and crime on every corner.

Tony was the youngest of Momma's kids. He had a light complexion and even at ten years old, he was a muscular little dude, always big for his age. He decided he wanted to play football when he was sitting on the front porch one day. All it took was for him to see a few kids running past the house up the street towards the park wearing their football equipment.

His older brother, Frank, at twelve was short and skinny the opposite of Tony. Frank wouldn't leave the house without creases ironed into his clothes. Tony, on the other hand, didn't care about none of that. Frank was brown skin and had brush waves. The two shared the same bedroom of their large brick, four-bedroom colonial home typical of the suburb, while their three older brothers shared the attic.

Tony shook his head trying to shake off sleep. "Yeah man, I'm alright. I just keep having the same kind of dream."

"What kind of dream?" Frank asked, looking at Tony.

"I'on know, man. We was all taking a trip to Dubai in this raw private jet."

"Ain't nothing wrong with dreaming about that, bra," Frank said brushing him off. "Least it wasn't something bad." He turned back to the window. "I think this yo' coach's truck pulling up in front of the house. You late?"

Tony jumped off the twin-sized bed and looked over Frank's shoulder. He saw his coach's black 4-door pickup truck parked out front. He threw on some shorts and ran downstairs.

Momma had a plate ready for him, along with the bacon he had been smelling there was grits, cheese eggs and pancakes. Tony ate Momma's breakfast like he was in a professional hotdog eating competition, not wanting his coach to have to wait too long for him.

He hugged and kissed Momma and headed out. Momma stood in the kitchen, dressed in her pink cotton robe with her silk scarf tied around her head and watched Tony dart out toward the front door.

"It's on y'all, see y'all after the game," Tony yelled at his brothers in the living room as he passed by.

"Alright, lil' bra, see you in a minute," Mell, Max and Stew yelled back at him.

Tony grabbed his football equipment out of the closet by the front door and left.

Tony tossed his football equipment in the bed of the pickup and climbed into the front seat.

"What's up, Coach Rick?" Tony said, breathing heavily as he buckled his seatbelt.

Coach Rick was the muni league football coach for the East Cleveland Chiefs and quickly became a father figure to Tony. Coach Rick was in his mid-thirties, light skin and bald. Coach Rick always kept a smile on his face, except when it was time for football. He took that very seriously.

"What's up boy, you ready for the game?" Coach Rick asked looking over at Tony in the passenger seat as he pulled off.

"Yeah, I'm ready. Who we play?" Tony asked.

"We play the Titans. They're undefeated just like us."

"Oh yeah," Tony nodded rubbing his hands together, "I'm ready Coach."

"If we win," Coach Rick glanced over at Tony, "we're going to Florida for the National Championship Game."

"Huh? You forreal?" Tony said, giving Coach Rick a shocked jaw-dropping look.

"Yeah. I'm serious, boy," Coach Rick said smiling. "This is a big game today."

"Oh yeah. I'm thirsty now. I'm 'bout to turn up."

Tony leaned forward turned up the radio and started singing the lyrics to Pastor Troy's song: *Weee ready. Weee ready. Weee ready for y'all.*

Coach Rick looked over at Tony with a big smile as he continued to sing and dance.

Back at the house, Frank was still upstairs in his bedroom looking out the window brushing his hair. His older brothers, Mell, Max and Stew were sitting on the floor in the living room with their eyes glued to the TV watching the Maury Show.

"Bet you that ain't his baby," Mell said looking at Max sitting next to him.

"Yes, it is dat nigga baby. They got the same egg ass head," Max said.

Stew laughed as Max and Mell continued to go back and forth.

Tony's three older brothers were all one year apart. Max, Mell and Stew were all brown skin with long cornrows that hung down their back. The three argued and fought every day with each other about little stuff. But whenever they were out in public, they'd always stuck together. Their bond was unbreakable as brothers. They loved each other to death no matter how much they argued or fought with each other.

Mell turned towards Max, extending his hand and said, "Alright. If it ain't his baby, I get to smack you and you can't tell Momma on me."

"Alright bet, but if it is his baby I get to smack you and Stew in the face wit' baby powder," Max said shaking Mell's hand.

"Naw nigga, don't put me in that shit. That's between y'all," Stew said.

The results are in . . .

They all turned their attention back to the television.

When it comes to two-year old Kayla . . .

This is Wayne Dawson of Fox 8 with breaking news.

"Aww . . . C'mon man," they said in unison.

We have breaking news on a local bank robbery attempt in East Cleveland. The suspect is said to be a black male in his mid-40's with a bald head approximately six-feet tall. If you live in the area, please lock your doors, the suspect is armed and dangerous.

"Momma! Mommaaa!" Frank came flying down the steps, and ran into the kitchen.

"What boy?" she said, she moved her cell phone away from her ear. "What's wrong wit' you?"

"I just saw Daddy through the window upstairs. He got a gun and he's coming on the porch."

"Quana, I'ma call you back. I gotta go," Momma said hurriedly, panic in her voice.

Momma ran from the kitchen into the living room. She ran past her boys and peeked out the blinds.

She saw her ex-husband, Stan whom she'd just broken up with and gotten a restraining order against because he started using crack again and physically abusing her. He had a look in his eyes she hadn't ever seen before in the seventeen years they'd been married.

"Oh my God," Momma said with fear in her eyes, her voice barely above a whisper.

She glanced over at her boys and her heart dropped into her stomach. She was in fear for her family's life. She tiptoed to the front door trying not to make a sound. She locked it, got on her knees and crawled over to be near her boys.

"What's wrong, Momma?" Stew asked.

"Daddy outside. He got a gun," Frank told them.

Stew jumped up. "Let him in! We ain't scared of him."

"Yeah!" Max chimed in.

"Shhh!" Momma pulled Stew back down. "No! Y'all just stay right here and be quiet," Momma said. She gathered her four boys up close and tried to wrap her arms around all of them, tears started welling up in her eyes.

"Don't worry y'all. He's gonna' leave if he thinks no one's home," Momma whispered.

Chapter Two

Stan tapped the door softly with the loaded .40 caliber three times. With each tap, Momma squeezed her boys tighter, tears running down her cheeks.

The intensity in the room was in ascension. The only sound you could hear was heavy breathing and heartbeats.

He knocked three more times.

Momma had her head down, squeezing her boys hoping he didn't come into the house.

Max and Stew stared at the doorknob ready for war. Stan shook it attempting to get in, but the door was locked tight and with the house being so quiet, he must've assumed no one was home. He turned around and left assuming no one was there because usually it sounded like a stampede of rhinos in the house with all the boys running around.

Mell heard his footsteps go across the wooden porch and down the steps.

"I think he's leaving, Momma," Mell said softly.

"Whew!" Momma exhaled in relief. "Thank you, Lord." And with that sigh of relief, her cell phone rang.

"Shit!" Momma said in an outburst, then covered her mouth and tried to quickly mute her phone.

Stan heard Momma's phone ring, he turned around, ran back up on the porch and pulled his gun out of his waistband.

Boom! Boom! Boom!

"Open this muthafuckin' door, bitch! I know you in there," Stan shouted as he kicked the door with his size thirteen steel-toed work boots.

Momma covered her mouth with her hands forcing herself not to make another sound. Stan was certain that she was home after he heard her phone ring from inside the house. He knew she didn't go anywhere without it.

"You got five seconds or I'm kickin' this mothafucka down!"

Momma continued to act as if she wasn't home. Suddenly the smoke detector went off loudly throughout the house.

"We out!" Mell said as he took off running first up the stairs. At every kick, the door weakened. Momma and the boys were running, tripping, and falling up the stairs over each other in a hurry to get out of way.

Without anyone noticing, Stew split from everyone and ran into the smoky kitchen, covering his mouth and nose with his shirt, he searched the kitchen looking for a knife.

"Damn Momma," he uttered to himself. He saw that she forgot to cut the fire off on the stove, leaving a pan of grease burning from the bacon she cooked.

He scrambled through the kitchen drawers. He coughed and wheezed not able to think over the loud smoke detector, and Stan's constantly kicking on the front door.

When Max realized Stew wasn't with them, he turned around and ran back down the steps. He heard his brother's cough coming from the kitchen. He went in there to find him.

"What you doing, bra?" Max said.

BANG!

They heard the door come off the hinges and hit the floor.

"Shhh... He in here," Stew whispered and put his index finger on his lip. He handed Max the butcher knife he'd found in the kitchen drawer. Then he grabbed the skillet of hot grease off the stove.

They ran and stood in the hallway by the steps figuring Stan would make a beeline straight to the attic. He knew that's where Momma always ran to hide when he tried to beat her.

Stew gave Max a head nod and whispered, "You ready?" Max nodded back.

They could hear each footstep Stan took as he got closer and closer to them, he was coming fast.

Max held the knife in one hand and with the other he counted down on his fingers. "Three. Two. One." They jumped out and shouted at the same time, "Bitch ass nigga!"

Stew slammed the hot grease into Stan's face just as he turned the corner.

"AHHHHH Shiiiit!" Stan screamed.

Pow! Pow! Shots recklessly rang out. Stan had pulled the trigger. Twice. One bullet hit the floor, the other hit the ceiling.

Hearing gunshots from the attic, Frank came running down the stairs at full speed heading into the living room to help his brothers. Max threw the knife at Stan's chest, but he missed. The knife flew across the room, grazed Frank's face, slicing his left cheek.

"Mommaaa!" Frank cried.

Momma came running down the stairs as fast as she could. Mell spotted his wooden bat that he had been rambling for from the time he'd entered the attic. He jumped down the entire flight of stairs, landing at Momma's heels.

Right then two police officers busted through the front door into the house with their guns drawn.

"Police! Put your hands where I can see them," the Officer said training his gun on Stan.

Stan didn't think twice. He darted through the living room, rushing he passed Frank, Max and Stew knocking them down and headed toward the back door. The police chased after him. As he headed toward the back, Mell jumped in his path and swung his bat one hard time hitting Stan directly on his temple knocking him out cold.

"Don't move!" the officer shouted.

"Keep your hands where we can see them," the other one said.

They restrained him, turned him face up and saw he wasn't going anywhere. He was unconscious.

"Code red. Code red," the officer spoke into his radio. "We need backup and paramedics on the scene." He looked at Stan. "We have the bank robbery suspect in custody. 10:4 over."

Momma was crying so hard she could barely think straight.

"Bank robbery? What is going on?" Momma sobbed. Then she noticed the blood running down Frank's cheek. "Oh lord! Look at my baby's face!" she cried.

Momma ran over to Frank and dropped to her knees. She held his face in the palms of her hands. "Jesus. Jesus. Jesus," she kept saying over and over.

"I'm alright, Momma," Frank said.

Frank looked over at his big brothers, Max, Stew and Mell and saw tears of anger on their faces. Max's eyes were red, and his hands were shaking like he was about to spaz out.

The paramedics, firefighters, and more officers arrived at the house. Even with all the commotion, Stan was still knocked out cold on the floor.

One officer had his knee in Stan's back restraining him until their backup arrived. The paramedics had to pull Frank out of Momma's arms and rushed him out of the house into the back of the EMS truck.

Max looked at his lil' brother being escorted out and it made him even more upset. He got up off the floor and ran toward defenseless Stan at full speed. "I'ma kill em," he screamed as he ran over and kicked him in the nose.

An officer snatched him off his feet. Max continued kicking and screaming. "I'ma kill 'em! I'ma kill 'em!" he yelled as the officer carried him outside.

A black female officer took Momma and her boys outside to question them.

"My name is Detective Nikki Jones," she said. "I'm just gonna take down some brief information for the police report." She turned to Momma. "May I have your name, please?" She took out her notebook ready to write.

But Momma, still really upset and crying, couldn't pull herself together enough to answer any questions.

Mell took control of the conversation and did all the talking.

"That's my momma, her name Kim, she ain't gon' talk right now but my name Mell," he said, without being prompted. "I'm fifteen."

"Uh-huh," the detective said nodding her head as she jotted it down in her notepad.

"This is my lil' brother, Stew," he said pointing at Stew standing next to him. "He fourteen. Oh yeah, and that's my other lil' brother over there, Max." He pointed over to Max as the officers continued to calm him down. "He thirteen."

"Okay, so there are three of you, correct?"

"Naw. It's more of us. I got two other lil' brothers. Frank and Tony. Frank over there in the ambulance truck. He just turned twelve, and our baby brother Tony. He only ten."

"Okay," she said. She continued writing in her notepad as Mell spoke.

"We have a sister named Quana, and we got a big brother name King. But they don't live with us, and King is in jail anyway."

"Wow," Officer Jones said. "Your mom has a lot on her plate. She must be a strong woman."

"Yeah. She is."

"Where is your baby brother, Tony?"

"He had a football game this morning. I'm just glad he wasn't here. If he was here during all of this, my Momma would have had a heart attack," Mell said to the detective.

Momma loved all her kids, but when it came to her baby boy, Tony, she was definitely biased.

Detective Jones looked at Momma and walked up to her. She stared into Momma's watery brown eyes, the tears rolling over Momma's black mole that sat on her cheek. "Stay strong, ma'am," she said and rubbed her on her back. "We have him in custody now so you and your boys are safe and out of harm's way."

Before they could get him out of the house, Stan regained consciousness. The officers read him his rights as they escorted him to the back of the police cruiser. He walked slowly and silently, his head down. His eyes were bloodshot red, high off of cocaine with blood running from his nose and skin peeling off his face from the scorching hot grease. Stan looked like a monster as he walked out of the house in handcuffs.

"Bitch ass nigga," Max yelled from the curb.

After the police put him in the backseat and drove Stan away, Momma told the boys to go in the house and clean up while she rode to the hospital with Frank. She still had a startled look on her face and it was easy to see that her mind was racing.

Quana pulled up with her son, Pierre. Quana was a spitting image of her mother, caramel skin complexion with a short blonde hair due just like Momma's. Pierre is Quana's twelve-year-old son. Pierre put you in the mind of OG Bobby Johnson's son from the movie South Central. Slim and dark skin.

"Quana," Momma said. "Stay here with the boys until I get back."

"Okay," she said. "But what happened?" Concern evident in her voice.

"I'll tell you when I get back."

Pierre jumped out of the car and ran to his grandmother squeezing her tight. "G'Momma, you alright? What you goin' to the hospital for?"

"I'm okay, baby. Just go in the house with your uncles."

Pierre ran into the house and saw the disaster. He started to ask what happened but saw the anger in his uncles' faces and could feel the tension in the room. He watched as they cleaned up and decided to help instead of bothering to ask any questions.

Quana was Momma's oldest child. Momma had given birth to her when she was just sixteen years old. Then she had her oldest boy, King, two years later. King and Quana had it rough growing up. At a young age Momma was hooked on drugs extremely bad.

King ran the streets of East Cleveland trying to sell dope, rob and steal to provide for his little brothers. He ended up spending his whole juvenile life in and out of the system.

While on drugs, Momma had only one best friend—the only person who hadn't judged her and loved her no matter what. She was down to do whatever, whenever. Her ride or die little sister, Tammie.

Tammie and Momma got high together, drunk together, lied together, stole, slept, smoke and ate together. Momma did nothing without Tammie and vice versa.

While Momma was out running the streets of East Cleveland with Tammie looking for ways to get high, she left Quana at home watching all the boys every day. Which forced Quana to become more of a mother figure to the boys than a big sister.

But one of those nights Momma's baby sister was killed, execution style by a dope boy she owed money to. When Momma lost her little sister, she felt like she'd lost everything. Like the world stopped. She didn't feel the urge to even live anymore.

One night soon after, Momma got home around 4am, high off crack, she fell back in her bed exhausted and stared at the ceiling. She cried, emotionally drained.

"Why? Why didn't you just take me instead, God? Why?" She cried and cried. Tears ran down her face as she thought of her little sister.

Still sobbing Momma looked up and saw her youngest, one-year-old, baby boy Tony, standing in her bedroom doorway holding his bottle with one hand and picking at his big round belly button with the other.

Tony just stood there and stared at her with his watery brown eyes. He was wearing nothing but a big wet diaper, never moving or making a sound, he just stood there staring at Momma, watching her cry.

She wiped the tears from her face and reached her arms out to him, and without hesitation, he ran and jumped into her arms, wrapping his little arms around her squeezing her with all the love in him. Momma never felt like that in her life. The feeling was better than any grade of crack she'd ever had. It was real, it was genuine, it was love and she knew that that was God's answer to her question.

That moment made her do a one hundred and eighty degree turn in her life. She started attending rehab meetings consistently, although she almost relapsed several times.

But she fought through it even through the toughest times like when she lost her mother on Christmas Day.

From there on out, Momma stayed clean to raise her boys.

Chapter Three

"This it right here, y'all," Coach Rick said yelling. He snatched his white towel from his shoulder and wiped the sweat from his bald head. The ninety-degree sun was giving his light complexion a slight tan.

"It's all or nothing, y'all," he continued. He was coaching the nine and ten-year old players where Tony played center and linebacker. They were all gathered around their coach in a huddle.

The East Cleveland Chiefs had been in existence for more than twenty-five years, but they weren't only a football team, they were family to each other.

In this game, the Chiefs took the lead and were winning by a touchdown with seven seconds left in the game. The opposing team, the Titans, had possession of the ball just five yards away from the end zone.

During a time out, the Chiefs' cheerleaders entertained the crowd. Performing at mid-field wearing their signature blue and orange uniforms complete with pom-poms. The scent of grilled hot dogs and hamburgers spread through the air and the stands were full of enthusiastic fans.

"Listen y'all, they only have enough time for one play," said Coach Rick as he held up his index finger to the boys. "One play, so I need y'all to go out there and leave everything y'all got on that field."

Coach Rick continued lecturing his young players with encouragement. Tony glanced into the bleachers and made eye contact with an older, dark skinned man with a full grey beard and muscles like a body builder. He was dressed head to toe in white. The man winked at Tony displaying his brilliant white smile.

Tony gleamed with excitement and nerves after noticing his Uncle Reggie sitting in the audience. Whenever a family member came to show their support Tony loved to show out so they could see something special.

Uncle Reggie was Momma's over protective big brother. He was a wild but meek drug dealer, and his name alone held clout throughout the city. There was always somebody after him. Enemies all over the city, but he knew how to handle and get out of any situation. Although Reggie did his dirt in the streets, he would not dare bring that kind of activity around Tony. He treated Tony like the son he never had.

After the cheerleaders ran back to the sideline, the two teams ran back onto the field for the last play of the game, the crowd erupted in excitement. Coach Rick had something on his mind.

"Hey Tony," he yelled. Tony stopped and turned around "Come here. Hurry up." Coach Rick waved him back in to the sideline. He sprinted over towards the sideline.

"What's up, Coach?"

Coach Rick got down on one knee, he grabbed Tony's facemask and looked directly into his eyes.

"Listen man, I need you to go out there and make a play for me, you hear me?"

"Yes sir."

"You know those dreams you told me you keep having?"

"Yeah," Tony said, shaking his head, looking deep into his coach's eyes.

"Well, I want you to know that dreams do come true if you really want them too." He had a serious tone to his voice. "Every play you make can get you a step closer to turning that dream into a reality."

Tony allowed that thought to sink into his mind while pondering the meaning of the words.

"Dreams do come true if you really want them too," Tony softly repeated to himself shaking his head as he stared into Coach Rick's eyes.

"I need you to get out there and make a play for me."

Tony gave Coach Rick a look of sincerity and with all the integrity he could muster. "I got you. I got you," Tony said. He started skipping backwards from the sidelines never breaking eye contact with his coach. "I got you," he repeated it over and over.

"Alright Tony, get out there and make it happen," yelled Coach Rick.

Tony turned and started to sprint onto the field, but tripped and fell face first into the grass.

"I told that boy about those shoestrings," Uncle Reggie laughed watching from the stands.

Tony jumped up on one knee, tucked his shoelace into his cleat and ran to his position at linebacker.

The Titans' quarterback was in a shotgun formation. He jammed his mouthpiece into his mouth while scanning the defense.

"Ready!" the quarterback yelled. He looked left, then right to check his receivers. "Set!" He lifted his knee, which sent his receiver in motion.

"Watch the reverse!" the safety, Shane, yelled to inform his teammates of the trick play. Tony's eyes were glued on the quarterback, like a hawk on its prey.

"GO!" The quarterback got the snap, he did a quick pump fake before dropping back and handing it to his receiver who was sprinting full speed across the backfield for the reverse. Tony shredded his block and blitzed behind the line of scrimmage.

"Eeeehhhwwww," the crowd roared, hearing the collision of Tony ramming his helmet into the receiver's facemask before he could make the next handoff. They hit the ground hard with such force that the ball popped out.

"Hell yeah, boy!" Uncle Reggie jumped up, chanted, and pumped his fist in the air.

"Fumble! Fumble!" Coach Rick screamed, but none of the players noticed that the ball popped out. He slammed his clipboard down, snapping it in half. "Get the damn ball!" Coach Rick screamed.

Shane and the Chiefs' outside linebacker, Ronald, ran and dove on top of the ball with five Titans players piling on top. With the ball buried underneath, and the game clock hitting regulation time, the referees blew their whistles ending the game.

"We did it! Oh shit, we did it!" Coach Rick his eyes grew to the size of golf balls as he realized they had won. They were going to the national championship.

"We're going to Florida!" he just kept saying quietly to himself.

Going to the National Championship was a huge accomplishment for Coach Rick, but not because of football, nor the championship game, but because it gave him a chance to get those kids out of East Cleveland at a young age and show them another part of the world. That was important to him.

East Cleveland is a city inside of a city. Extreme poverty and violence like any other ghetto. But what was so different and dangerous about it, was the addictiveness to come back. Even though it was filled with troubles, no one left the city without returning. And anyone raised in East Cleveland was loyal and attached to the City itself. Coach Rick wanted to change that for these boys.

Over time, as Coach Rick worked with Tony, he became his favorite. He could see his athleticism, strength, dedication, dominance and loyalty at a young age. Because of that, he took Tony under his wing and treated him as his own.

From there on out, Coach Rick provided the transportation necessary to get Tony to all of his games.

Chapter Four

"You showed up out there today, baby boy!" Uncle Reggie said. He walked his nephew through the partially empty parking lot after the game.

"Shoot, I had too. I wasn't 'bouta let them beat us," Tony said. Carrying his football equipment in one hand, he shoved the hotdog he got from the concession stand into his mouth with his other hand.

"Yeah, but you almost broke your neck, too." Uncle Reggie laughed. "What did I tell you about them shoestrings," he said, palming the top of Tony's head like a basketball.

"I know, I thought they was tied up. Man that stuff hurt when I fell."

"Yeah, I bet it did!" Uncle Reggie chuckled, his hand rested on the top of Tony's big head. They walked to Uncle Reggie's clean, decked out, all black, Astro van.

"M-Man where the f-f-fuck this is dude at?"

"Shut the fuck up, here he come," the other jack boy said pulling his ski mask over his face.

The two young jackers, Marv and Rico, had been staked out in the back of Uncle Reggie's Astro van for about an hour.

Ricco had a bad stuttering problem especially when he was nervous and Marv had a more aggressive mentality. You could tell this wasn't his first robbery.

Their original plan was only to break into the van and steal his music, but once they got into the van, they decided to wait inside for Reggie to return and stick him for his cash. Ricco thought it was dumb, but went along with Marv's plan anyway.

"If this nigga play crazy we killin' his dumbass," Marv said cocking his pistol.

"Why we g-g-gotta . . . um shoot him? Let's just g-g-get the m-money and..."

"Man, shut yo' scary, stuttering ass up," Marv said cutting him off.

Man I knew I shoulda never brung this bitch ass nigga on this move with me. His scary ass gon fuck everything up, Marv thought.

"M-man this the last t-time I'm doing . . ."

Chirp. Chirp.

Ricco stopped mid-sentence when he heard the door unlock. He felt his heart drop to his stomach.

"Here we go." Marv smiled eagerly and got himself ready for action. The two jack boys ducked down behind the third row of the seats.

"Shotgun!" Tony yelled as he ran around to the other side of the van. He yanked the handle, snatching the door open and jumped into the front seat.

Uncle Reggie routinely looked underneath his van before entering, checking for any type of tracking devices. Once he saw it was clear, he jumped in and put the key into the ignition.

"If you start this bitch up, I'ma splatter yo' brains all over the windshield," Marv said in a serious low tone of voice as he pressed the cold steel barrel to the back of Uncle Reggie's head. Tony shifted in his seat pressing his shoulders against the passenger door, mouth and eyes wide open his eyebrows raised up in fear.

"Aye, get the lil' nigga. Make sho' he don't try no funny shit," Marv ordered looking at Ricco.

"Don't touch my nephew," Uncle Reggie said in an intimidating voice facing forward with his hands on the steering wheel.

"Shut the fuck up, old ass nigga," he said squeezing his lips tight as he threateningly mugged the steel deeper into the back of Uncle Reggie's skull. "Get the lil' nigga," Marv barked at Ricco again.

The tension in the van was crushing. Ricco grew uncomfortable as he noticed the menacing scowl in Uncle Reggie's eyes through the rearview mirror.

"He-he-he cool man," Ricco told Marv, with his stutter coming out stronger. Even though they were the ones with the gun, the look in Uncle Reggie's eyes scared the shit out of Ricco. He was afraid to lay a hand on Tony. "I-I'm w-w-watching him."

Tears built up in Tony's eyes, he started breathing heavily.

"Check this out," Uncle Reggie said still facing forward with his hands on the steering wheel. "Now we can do this the easy way or the hard way. Look out that right window back there."

Marv gained a look of suspicion. He looked back and forth at Ricco, then Uncle Reggie. He gave Ricco a head nod, telling him to check the window. Ricco pulled the curtain back and peaked out the window as he listened to Uncle Reggie's raspy intimidating voice.

"Y'all see that black Honda sitting down there?"

Marv listened but he kept his pistol mounted to the back of Uncle Reggie's head.

"If I hit my brake pedal three times that A.R he got in there is gonna turn you two lil' niggas into ramen noodles. Now look out the other side."

Marv nodded towards the other window. Ricco dropped his pistol out of his fidgety hand onto the backseat. He jumped over to the other side of the van.

"See that white Tahoe?"

Marv looked at Ricco. Ricco looked like he was about to shit in his pants.

Marv knew that his little Smith & Wesson stood no chance to the heavy artillery that Uncle Reggie had already described.

"Now what my dude got in there is gon' turn y'all two lil' niggas into tomato sauce," Uncle Reggie continued as he stared through the rear view mirror right into Ricco's eyes with a look that could kill.

"Now I know y'all young and don't know no better and that's the only reason I'ma spare y'all. But pulling this shit in front of my nephew got me tempted to turn y'all into spaghetti and have you lil' niggas for dinner tonight."

The smell of shit invaded Marv's nostrils.

"N-n-n-no . . . We-we . . . um sorry," Ricco said as he snatched off his mask, yanked the door open and took off running.

Marv, looking lost and confused thinking to himself. *I can't believe this nigga jus bounced on me, I gotta get out the fuck out of here. This old nigga ain't nobody to fuck with.* Marv looked at the van door wide open, jumped out darted through the parking lot.

Tony couldn't believe what he'd just seen.

"You alright, baby boy?" Uncle Reggie said, trying to comfort his nephew.

Tony didn't respond, he sat there in the same position with his back pressed against the passenger door, mouth still wide open. He'd never seen a real gun in his life let alone a robbery taking place right in front of his young eyes. This situation could haunt Tony forever and Uncle Reggie was well aware of that.

Uncle Reggie was pissed. *I can't believe them lil' niggas tried that shit in front of my nephew,* he thought.

Good thing Uncle Reggie payed attention to his surroundings and remembered the color, make, and model of the two abandoned cars he had noticed when he walked through the parking lot after the game.

"What you just saw, you gon' have to deal with your entire life if you don't get out of this city," Uncle Reggie said. "And it ain't just gon' happen. You gotta make it happen." He turned and looked at Tony as his doors automatically shut with a press of a button.

"We all got choices, and the choices that you make is what's gon' shape yo' life. But first, understanding that you even have a choice is the key."

Tony stared out of the window, thinking about Uncle Reggie's words as they cruised down Lee Road, bumping Jay-Z's, *Reasonable Doubt.*

Chapter Five

"Aye y'all, I'm 'bouta go to AJ's. I'll be back," Mell said running out of the front door. AJ's was the corner store at the end of the street.

Tony, Frank, and Max sat on the living room floor eating syrup sandwiches, watching *Menace to Society*.

Stew was stretched out across the sofa on the house phone talking to Tasha, a pretty, brown-skinned girl from Shaker Heights he met after one of his games. Although Stew was only a fourteen-year-old freshman in high school, he attracted women who were twice his age. Tasha, one of those women, was a registered nurse in her twenties.

"You gonna come to my game tomorrow?" Stew asked.

"I caaaannn't," she whined, drawing out the words. "I have to work tomorrow."

"Just tell em' you sick or something'," Stew said, making her giggle.

"No boy, it don't work like that . . . buuutttt, I do wanna see you this weekend." She teased him in a sexy tone enticing him. "So you better be ready boy."

"Man what you talkin' bout, I'm always ready," Stew said blushing with his hands in his pants.

"Mommaaa!" Tony jumped up and charged her as she came through the front door from working a double shift at her nursing home job. Tony hugged her tight as if he had not seen her in months.

"Hey my baby," Momma said as she hugged and kissed his forehead

She sat her purse down on the table and fell back on the living room sofa. Tony unlaced her shoes and removed them from her overworked, aching feet.

"Whew," she said in relief.

"Thank you baby. Hand me the mail off that table." Momma said while unbuttoning her work shirt. "Stew go take that trash outside it's stinking up my whole house!"

"Man, you can't tell Max to do it?"

"No, because I told you to. And who in the hell are you calling a man?" Momma screamed.

"Yeah nigga, who you callin' a man," Max said teasing his brother.

"Oh my God man, I'ma call you back," Stew slammed the house phone down, kicked Max in the leg and stormed into the kitchen. Tony ran over and handed Momma the mail from the dining room table.

"How was your game last week?" Momma asked Tony as she thumbed through an impressive amount of college recruiting letters for Stew.

"It was too fun. Uncle Reggie was there. I made somebody fumble, and we won!"

"Alright! You go boy!" She smiled raising her hand giving Tony a high five. Her smile quickly diminished when she came across some mail from the bank about her house being foreclosed.

Tony went on and on not noticing Momma's frustration.

"Coach Rick said he coming to pick me up Friday because we..."

"I know baby, I know," Momma said cutting him off. She sent Tony upstairs to get her reading glasses as she opened the mail.

"Who is it?" Momma screamed in a frustrated tone after hearing a knock at the door.

"It's me open the door!"

Max and Frank jumped up and ran to the door after hearing their uncle's voice.

"What up, Uncle Reggie?" the boys said. They were all smiling and play fighting with their uncle.

"W'sup wit' y'all sucka's?" he said as he shadowboxed with them. The boys always got excited when Uncle Reggie came through. He would wrestle with them and then make them wrestle and fight each other for hours. Then he'd always give them a few dollars to split after he felt they had been roughed up enough.

"What's wrong with you?" Uncle Reggie said as he walked into the living room looking at Momma with a concerned expression.

"Nothing, I'm fine," she said in a tone that indicated otherwise. He could sense that Momma had just gotten some bad news. He looked down at her sitting on the couch like she had just had the longest day of her life.

Mail was scattered on her lap, with her depressing demeanor that allowed him to assume it was some financial issue. Without hesitation, he pulled out fifteen hundred dollar bills and slipped them slyly into her purse without her noticing.

Chapter Six

"Uncle Reggieee!" Tony shouted, he came running down the stairs.

"There go my boy!" Uncle Reggie said, smiling from ear to ear. Tony handed Momma her reading glasses then ran, jumped up and start doing pull ups on Uncle Reggie's big arms as he lifted Tony up and down with ease.

"AHHHHH!" Mell cried as he came bursting through the front door falling into the doorway with a swollen eye and a busted lip.

"What da fuck happened to you, boy?" Uncle Reggie asked with concern.

"What happened? Who did this?" Momma cried.

"Man, them dudes...them dudes in the corner house," Mell said crying.

A few weeks before, four brothers between nineteen and twenty years old moved into the neighborhood. They had come from the Projects and moved into the big blue house that sat on the corner end of the street right next to AJ's. There had been conflicts there ever since they moved in.

The four brothers sat on their front porch steps looking for trouble. Between smoking Black and Mild's and drinking they would harass the customers leaving the store.

One day the four brothers saw an eighty-year-old lady leaving out of the store. They snatched her cane and tossed it on top of the roof laughing at the woman as she sat on the curb helpless.

Max and his best friend lil' Chuck, who lived across the street from Momma and the boys, walked to the store together.

The four brothers began throwing acorns at them. Later that night Max and Lil' Chuck snuck out of the house to throw two large bricks right through their front living room window then run away.

The four brother watched Max and Chuck run away and they caught Mell slipping, walking to the store alone, thinking he was Max because they looked so much alike.

"Quit cryin' lil' Nigga. What corner house?" Uncle Reggie said as he snatched Mell up by his shirt collar looking into his eyes.

"Down the street by the corner store, man," Mell cried. Blood drippin' from his lip.

"Come on!" Uncle Reggie said, walking out the door. "Max and Stew put y'all shit on," he said.

Stew was already lacing his shoes and Max took off up the stairs to grab his brass knuckles he'd found at the park a few weeks ago.

Momma was worried, scared, confused, and nervous all in one. Frank and Tony ran behind them.

"Get y'all asses back in here," Momma yelled stopping them from going with their big brothers to fight.

Uncle Reggie and the boys stormed out of the house. Mell's T-shirt was ripped up. Stew had on a wife beater and some black basketball shorts, and Max was shirtless.

All three boys had their braids twisted straight to the back with a look of retaliation on their faces.

They walked at a quick pace, following Uncle Reggie down the street.

"Shit! I gotta get the fuck outta here," Lil' Chuck said with a strong lisp as he looked out his bedroom window, watching them march down the street. He was on punishment all the time but in a situation like this he had to sneak out without a doubt.

"Fuck dat! One fight, we all fight," Lil' Chuck said to himself as he ran out his house and took off down the street. He was shirtless, and his long braids flew in the wind. He ran fast in the middle of the street to catch up with Uncle Reggie and the boys.

"Put y'all shoes on," Momma told Tony and Frank as she ran up the stairs. "I be damn if them grown muthafucka's gonna put they hands on mines," she said to herself. She quickly undressed out of her work uniform. Frank and Tony put their shoes on and waited down stairs by the door.

"Go get in the car," Momma yelled at Frank and Tony as she came running down the stairs in a grey sweat suit. She carried Mell's wooden bat with a brown scarf wrapped tight around her head.

Tony and Frank jumped in the back of Momma's silver caravan.

"Put y'all seatbelts on."

She sped off down the street. When they arrived, Momma nearly went into shock—it was complete pandemonium. Four fights were going on at once. Uncle Reggie stood on the sidewalk coaching his nephews.

"Mell flip his ass over right now!" Uncle Reggie screamed watching Mell take blows to his face. It was never a such thing as an unfair match, age or size didn't matter to Uncle Reggie and he always encouraged his nephews never to be scared to fight nobody.

"Mell flip his ass over right now!" Uncle Reggie said again. He stood over them fighting in their front yard, Mell wiggled and squirmed fast trying to get out the bottom position, but it was no match. The dude was twice his size.

On the sidewalk, Max was mounted on top of one of the brothers screaming, "BITCH! BITCH!" every time his fist connected to his face.

Stew and Lil' Chuck was in the middle of the street in an all-out slugfest going blow for blow with the grown men from the Projects. All four of them had busted lips.

The second Momma pulled up and saw all that was going on, she jumped out with the bat screaming, "Oh, hell no!" She had left the van door open she was moving so fast. She went running toward the chaos with the bat cocked behind her head.

"What the hell you think you doin'?" Uncle Reggie yelled holding her back with one forearm. "Take yo' ass back up the street," he said.

Momma screamed trying to move his arm out of her way to protect her boys. "No! He is too big to be fighting him," Momma yelled watching Mell get pounced on by the 20-year-old dude. "Get the hell off my baby!" Momma cried. She threw the bat over Uncle Reggie's shoulder trying to get the dude off her child.

Tony and Frank got out the van together and ran over towards Momma when suddenly they heard loud police sirens coming through the neighborhood. It sounded like twenty police cruisers heading straight towards them.

"Oh shit!" Uncle Reggie shouted. "That's enough! Get in the van. Hurry up. The police comin'."

The boys continued fighting ignoring the sirens. Max got up off the dude he was fighting leaving him knocked out on the sidewalk. He picked Mell's bat up that Momma threw from out the grass and ran full speed into the front yard.

"BITCH!" he said swinging the bat knocking the big dark skin man from off the top of Mell. The bat knocked him out cold, Mell flipped him over and gave him a dose of his own medicine as he laid there defenseless.

"Get the fuck out of the van!" Uncle Reggie demanded. The boys heard the anger in their uncle's voice and knew it was time to go, so they got their last hits in.

"Hoe ass nigga," lil' Chuck said as he spit blood and mucus into the dude's face before he ran and jumped into the van behind Stew.

Momma skirted off from the scene and headed back home. Tony sat squashed in the middle of his brothers. He looked and listened to everybody as they talked about going back for more.

Chapter Seven

"Come on y'all, hurry up we gone be late," Momma yelled as all the boys scrambled around the house, rushing trying to get ready to go to Stew's football game."

"I can't find my other shoe," Frank shouted.

"It's under my bed" Max screamed from his bedroom as he got dressed.

"Where is the iron at?" Mell yelled.

"Boy, you ain't got no time to be ironing," Momma said, cutting him off.

"If y'all ain't in the car in the next two minutes, y'all staying home," Momma yelled. She walked down the stairs and saw Tony sitting on the bottom step of the stairwell waiting to leave.

"Come on baby," she said, walking passed him.

Tony jumped up. "Shotgun!" he yelled and ran outside and jumped into Momma's van. She and Tony went and sat in the van and waited for the rest of the boys. Momma's phone rang.

"Hello?" She flipped open her cell phone.

"Where you at?" Quana said. She and Pierre stood in the crowded parking looking around for Momma's minivan.

"We on our way. We'll be there in a minute."

"Alright. Bye, Ma," Quana said nonchalantly. She hung up and walked to the bleachers to find a seat.

The rest of the boys came rushing out the door and jumped in the van. Momma headed straight down Euclid Avenue, a main road in East Cleveland.

Momma pulled up into Shaw stadium parking lot. After searching, they finally found a parking spot and made their way to the entrance.

Momma wore her red T-shirt. It had the number fifty-five on the back of it with "Stew's Mom" printed above it in big black bold letters.

Tony and Frank walked by Momma's side while Mell and Max tailed them, strutting through the parking lot. They entered the stadium and saw that both the Home and Away sections were filled to capacity. In the Skybox seats were division one recruits such as Ohio State, Clemson, Alabama, and Arizona State. Shaw's band was performing at their best. They played the high school's theme song, while the highlighters danced away to the band's music.

"There go G'Momma!" Pierre yelled and pointed. He spotted them coming in through the entrance gate. Momma and the boys walked over to join Quana and Pierre.

"Heyyyyy Momma!" Stew's teammates waved and yelled from the bench as Momma and the boys walked passed.

Nearly everybody in East Cleveland called Momma, Auntie or Momma.

"MOMMAAA!" Stew pulled his mouth guard out smiled and threw both arms up in the air.

"Let's go, baby," Momma said as she pumped her fists in the air. Tony got excited every time he saw Stew in his football uniform. Shaw was down on the scoreboard by two touchdowns. Stew was putting on an outstanding performance defensively.

"What we miss?" Momma asked. She sat down next to Quana.

"He made some good tackles. He's doing really good," Quana replied, she took one of Pierre's nachos out of his bag and ate it.

Tony was on the edge of his seat. As the game went on, he calculated all Stew moves and techniques as he dominated his opponent through each quarter. Using swim moves, spin moves, and bull rushes. His finesse was just an extra attribute added to his strength.

Momma, Quana and the boys quickly jumped up out of their seats when they saw Stew running off the field, screaming in pain as he held his hand.

They all ran down to the lowest level of the stands directly behind the bench to see if he was okay.

They leaned over the wall to get his attention but he could not see nor hear them with the vibrancy of the stadium surrounding them. Tony ran back up to his seat and stood on his tippy toes to get a better view. He saw Stew extend his arm towards the trainers, squeezing his eyes shut tight in pain.

"Ahhhhh! Just put it back in place!" Stew screamed. The trainer quickly examined his hand and noticed his pinky finger was completely out of socket, going into two different directions. He couldn't take the pain but more importantly, he wanted to get back in the game so he had to. Stew bit his bottom lip down hard and shut his eyes tight. He snapped his finger back into place and then ran back onto the field.

"What the..." Tony said with an astonished expression on his face. Stew continued playing like nothing ever happened. Tony stared at Stew as though he wasn't human.

"Hello!" Momma said as she flipped open her cell phone.

"Hey, Momma. This is Coach Rick."

"Oh hey, Coach Rick" she said plugging her index finger into her ear to tune out the loud noise from the stadium.

"We leaving for the game tomorrow morning and I am just calling to let you know that I'll be able to get Tony later this evening. Like it said on the permission slip, all the players will be spending the night at my house."

"Okay. That's fine. I'll be home in a few hours after Stew's game," Momma said. She hung up and tuned back into the game. Stew had eleven tackles and three sacks despite their loss. He'd put on an outstanding performance for the fans and the scouts.

After the game Quana, Momma, and the boys lingered near the gate waiting for Stew to come out of the locker room.

"Alright bye, Ma. I'm getting ready to go, my feet hurt," Quana said, throwing her purse strap over her shoulder.

"Ma? Can I go over G'Momma house?" Pierre asked his mother.

"Yeah, you can come over," Momma said before Quana could even answer.

Tony sprinted over to Stew as he came walking from out of the locker room with a white towel on his head.

"What's up lil' bra?" Stew said as he displayed his big white smile.

"Man you was doggin' them boys out there!" Tony said as him and Stew slapped hands and hugged.

"Good lookin' lil' bra!" He rubbed his hand on the top of Tony's head as they walked towards his Momma.

"Man that stuff ain't hurt when you broke your hand?" Tony asked, looking up to his brother.

Stew laughed. "Yeah, it hurt, but I had to fight through it. You can't be soft out there on that field."

"Man!" Tony said as he shook his head from side to side.

"Whoop-whoop! Whoop-whoop!" Momma said pumping her arms up as Stew walked up on her and his brothers. Stew laughed.

"Stop doing that Momma," he said.

Hugging her. They rocked from side to side hugging.

"Good game bra," Mell said.

"Yeah, good game boy," Max slapped Stew hard on his butt.

"Man, stop playin' wit' me for I beat yo' ass, nigga."

Stew quickly turned around and flinched at Max.

Tony, Mell, and Frank laughed.

"Hey strangerrr." A sexy voice came from behind him.

Stew turned around and saw Tasha standing there like a model wearing short jean shorts with her booty cheeks hanging out resting her hands on her hip.

Stew thought to himself as he looked at her nipple rings through her tank top. He wanted to talk but the words wouldn't come out. The only thing on his mind was the last time they made out and how she put it on him.

"W'sup," Stew said, smiling at the half-naked female.

Momma looked the girl up and down. "Excuse me. Who are you?" Momma interrupted.

Not only didn't Momma hate the fact Tasha didn't speak to everyone when she walked up, but her being half naked and flirting with her fourteen-year-old child was a huge problem to Momma.

Tasha's smile quickly converted into a mug. "I'm Tasha. Who is you the fuck?" she replied with a nasty tone.

"Listen, you fast ass lil' girl. Next time you walk up on somebody, you say excuse me and introduce yourself," Momma said pointing her finger in Tasha's face.

"Chill, Momma. You trippin'," Stew said.

"Lil' girl?" Tasha said, rolling her head. "I'm twenty-two years old. I am a grown ass woman!"

Momma leaned in closer as she squinted her eyes real low. "Listen here, this is the first and the last time that I am going to tell you this, you stay the hell away from my son."

"Man, Momma you trippin'," Stew said, embarrassed walking away from the commotion.

"Go get in the van!" Momma yelled following behind Stew. All the boys followed and jumped into the van. Tasha stood there staring as Momma sped out of the parking lot exasperated.

"You stay the hell away from that girl. Don't ever let me see you talking to her or with her or about that girl." Momma pointed a finger at Stew. "Do you understand me? I don't even want you thinking about that girl!"

Stew shook his head as they drove up Euclid Avenue, looking defeated.

Chapter Eight

"Aye y'all. Come look at this pineapple tree?" Tony said rubbing the bark of a 30-foot palm tree. The team's hotel suite was right off the ocean. These kids had never seen such beautiful scenery.

"That's a palm tree," Coach Rick said as he stood on the hotel balcony looking down at the boys smiling, embracing the moment.

"Come on up y'all, the game start in an hour." All the boys raced to up to the room to get ready for the locally televised championship game. It was the first time on TV for them, even if it was only being shown in another state.

Back in Cleveland . . .

Stew sat on the front porch steps on the cordless house phone as he watched his friends and brothers play a pickup game of 3 on 3. They pulled their basketball hoop from the backyard into the street. All six boy had their shirts off as the sun beamed down on their bare skin.

"It's me, Frank and Pierre against y'all three," Mell said as he dribbled the ball back and forth through his legs.

"Alright. C'mon nigga. Check ball," Max said, standing in front of him.

"I'm checking Pierre," Chris yelled. "Lil' Chuck you check Frank," Chris said as he ran up on Pierre pulling his shorts up and getting into a defensive stance.

Chris was the spoiled kid who lived next door to Momma and the boys. He wasn't athletic at all but he was down to play football, basketball, manhunt or any other games with the boys. He grew so close to the family, Momma start treating him like her own.

Momma sat in the TV room on her cellphone. She was going through mail when she came across a letter from Stan. "Quana, I'ma call you back," Momma said. She hung up and pulled the notebook paper out of the envelope.

I'm keep this short and straight to the point. You the reason I have to spend the next twelve years of my life in here. All you had to do was open the fuckin' door, dumb bitch. Now you gone suffer tryna raise all them stupid muthafuckas on yo' own. None of them will never be shit. I hope they drive yo' dumb ass crazy. And while you at it, find out who the fuck Tony real father is.

Tears fell down Momma's cheeks as she balled up the letter and threw it across the room onto the other sofa.

"Stewart!" Momma yelled.

"Yeah, Momma," Stew said. He came through the front door with his phone to his ear.

"Run upstairs and get my cigarettes and lighter out my purse."

"Alright . . ." He paused when he noticed her crying. "What's wrong, Momma? You alright?"

"Yeah. I'm fine," Momma said trying to hide her emotions.

Stew ran upstairs and brought Momma her purse. She sparked up a cigarette and started flicking though channels.

Stew went back on the front porch and sat on the bottom steps rolling dice on the ground. He watched as Mell and boys played 3 on 3 in the street.

Chris went up for a layup, and the ball went over the entire backboard.

"Ahh foul, man," Chris screamed. Stew laughed.

"Nigga ain't nobody even touch you, you was wide open."

The cordless phone rang. "Hello," Stew answered still laughing at the move Chris tried to pull.

"Hey! Please. Please. Please! I need your help." It was Tasha. She was crying uncontrollably. Stew facial expression immediately became solemn he dropped the dice down and replied with concern evident.

"What's up? What happened? What's wrong?" Stew said. He never heard her cry before. He definitely hadn't heard her the way she was sounding now.

"Please. Baby please! I just really need you to help me. I need to come get you. I messed up! I messed up!" she cried.

"Okay, calm down. I'm already outside. Call me when you get close. I'm waitin' on you."

"Oh, God. Please, baby. Thank you so, so much I'm on my way," she said.

Stew hung up the cordless phone and stared at it thinking what could possibly have her crying like that. Then minutes later Tasha called back and told Stew she was on the next street waiting for him. Stew dropped the phone on the front porch stairs and ran through the shortcut in the backyard to the next street over. He stood on the curb as Tasha sped up on him in her red Honda. He jumped in the car.

"What's up? What happened to you?" Stew said looking at the scratches on her neck and face. She was drenched in sweat, like she had just jumped out the shower and her high complexion made the small scratches stand out.

"I promise I don't know. I just blacked out and I need your help," she cried as she sped down Euclid.

"Alright slow down before we get pulled over," Stew said looking back and forth at her and the road with a WTF look on his face.

Back at the house, Uncle Reggie stopped by to pay Momma and the boys a visit. He sat in the TV room with Momma reminiscing about their mother and baby sister, Tammie.

"I will never forget we was about thirteen or fourteen," Momma said laughing. "I did something that pissed her off one day, and the next morning when Mommy woke us up for school we got dressed and I went to slide my foot in my boot. I felt a puddle of warm..."

Uncle Reggie bust out laughing. "Ahhhahaa. Hell naw! She pissed in yo' shoe!" he said cracking up. He and Momma laughed.

"Thank you for tuning in with our 5 O'clock News. Our opening story is a local Pop Warner football team from East Cleveland."

"Shit! Turn it up that's baby boys' team down in Florida," Uncle Reggie said.

Momma quickly increased the volume to the max.

"Stew, Mell, all y'all come here. Hurry up!" she yelled.

The boys stopped hooping and ran in the house. Lil' Chuck and Chris followed them.

REPORTER: *The young nine and ten-year-old boys from East Cleveland, Ohio, are bringing the first National Championship trophy back in their city.*

"YEAHHH!"Uncle Reggie, Mell and the boys said in celebration as they showed highlights of the game.

In the background, the report continued. "Right here I have with me the MVP defensive player of the game."

"Shhhh! Be quiet. Be quiet." Momma waved her hand to quiet everybody down so she could here Tony speak.

"Be quiet y'all. Tony 'bouta talk," Max said.

Everyone stared at the TV listening while the reporter spoke into the microphone with Tony standing beside her. "You were flying all over the field out there," she said. "Where did you get the skills and energy to be running across the field on every tackle?"

"I was just thirsty," Tony said and shook his head from side to side.

"There you have. Great job and congratulations on being a national champion."

"Thanks," Tony said, then ran off camera to go back and celebrate with his team.

"Man. Tony raw," Frank and Chris said in unison.

Momma stared at the TV screen amazed at what she just saw, still not believing her eyes.

The boys ran back out the front door talking about Tony, then went back to their game of three on three basketball.

Chapter Nine

Tasha pulled up to her three-story brick villa in Shaker Heights.

Damn this look like an NBA player's crib, Stew thought to himself.

Tasha pulled in the long driveway into the backyard. She slammed on the breaks, jumped out and power walked to her back door.

Stew jumped out the car and followed her into the house.

"Oh, shit!" He stopped right in his tracks. He couldn't believe what he saw. "What the fuck did you do?" Stew said with a jaw dropping expression on his face.

Tasha didn't answer she just cried and cried. Stew stood there with his mouth opened staring at the dead body on Tasha's kitchen floor.

"I made a mistake," she cried pacing back and forth in the kitchen, she ran her hand from front to back through her long wet sweaty hair.

Tasha had executed her husband to inherit the money from his life insurance policy. A wealthy forty-two year old white man, he was a doctor at the Cleveland Clinic.

"Take me back to the house," Stew said. "I don't want nothing to do with this shit, man."

"No! Please. Just help me put him somewhere," she pleaded.

"Hell naw! You trippin'! What you mean put him somewhere? I can't fix this."

"Just help me put him in the car," Tasha said as she ran upstairs. Stew looked at her like she was crazy as she ran up the wooden stairs barefoot.

"Take me back home right now! I'm cool." He shook his head side to side, looking down at the body. She came back down with a sheet and started wrapping up his body.

This girl crazy, Stew thought to himself, slowly walking backwards and staring at her with a sense of fear in his eyes. Tasha wrapped her husband's body like it wasn't her first time.

"Okay, come on. Help me put him in the trunk," she said as she picked up his upper body. She had her hands under his armpits, dragging him and walking backwards out the back door to the trunk of the car.

"Come on, baby. Help me grab his legs," Tasha begged. She threw him in the trunk and jumped in the car.

"Take me home right now. Fuck this!" Stew said as he shut the passenger door.

"Okay," she said, looking backwards backing out of the driveway. She skirted off from her house, speeding through the city at 50mph looking for the best place to dump the body.

She pulled up and parked her car by a wooded area in the park right up the street from Stew's house.

"What you doing? Take me home!" he said, looking at her crazy. Tasha ignored him, she got out and started pouring gasoline in the trunk all over her husband.

"Hell naw, I'm out!" Stew jumped out and took off running. As he ran, he looked back and saw Tasha's car go up in flames. He ran as fast as he could down the hill as his braids flew in the wind with a million thoughts running through his mind. The image of the man's body was stuck in his head. He ran and ran, making it home was all he wanted.

"911. What's your emergency?"

"Oh, gosh! Some kid just set this car on fire!" The woman yelled.

"Okay, where is the car and what is your name?"

"My name is Tynetta Johnson. The car is at Forest Hill Park parking lot! Hurry!"

"Ma'am, did you see the suspect or which direction he ran?"

"Yes!" she screamed. "He's running down the hill towards Euclid Avenue wearing a red shirt with long braids!"

"Thank you, ma'am. Police and firemen are on the way."

Tasha stopped disguising her voice and hung up the phone as she left the park. A few hours prior, she reported her car stolen to the police to eliminate herself as a potential suspect.

Max and Lil' Chuck sat on the porch watching Mell, Chris, Pierre, and Frank play horse in the street.

"Where you comin' from?" Max asked as he saw Stew running from up the street.

"Nowhere," he said leaning forward with his hands on his knees, sweating breathing hard trying to catch his breath.

"Why you outta breath like that, you was throwing rocks at cars or somthin' nigga?"

Before Stew could answer, two police cars pulled in the front yard.

"SHIT!" Lil' Chuck said before he jumped over the banister and hit the shortcut through the backyard.

"You in the red shirt! Get on your knees and keep your hands where I can see them!"

Stew dropped to his knees and locked his hands together on the back of his head. Momma and Uncle Reggie came running outside when they heard the police screaming through the bullhorn.

"What the fuck is this?" Uncle Reggie asked.

"What are y'all doing to my baby?" Momma cried, running off the porch.

"Ma'am, get back on the porch. We'll explain everything in a moment," the officer said as they pointed their weapons at Stew, slowly walking up behind him.

"Momma, I swear I didn't do nothing! I swear!" Stew yelled as they cuffed him and took him into custody.

"Can somebody tell me what's goin' on?" Momma cried.

"Yes ma'am, just stay right there, we'll talk to you in a second."

Stew was transferred to a juvenile detention center where he sat for two months. He was charged with involuntary manslaughter. During the process, he lost all of his college football offers and was sentenced to five years in ODYS.

Momma and the boys were hurt, lost, and incomplete without Stew.

Tony was devastated. He had no understanding of how his big brother that he looked up to the most would leave him.

Tony, his siblings, and Momma went together every weekend to visit him. The US Marshals caught up with Tasha in Akron, Ohio.

She was found guilty of first-degree murder and arson and was sentenced to life in prison.

Chapter Ten

Five years later . . .

On September 5th, Tony's sixteenth birthday, King and Stew were released from jail. Momma put together a birthday/welcome home party for her sons at Uncle Bunky's house.

Uncle Bunky was Momma's oldest brother, she'd come from a big family, too.

Momma hired a live DJ and set up tents in her brother's backyard. Family and friends were mingling, eating, laughing, and talking.

Uncle Reggie was on the grill. 'Cueing up hotdogs and burgers as he rapped the lyrics to Notorious B.I.G.

"It was all a dream, I used to read 'Word Up' magazine..." He vibed as the music thumped through the speakers.

Tony had had a rapid growth spurt in the last few years. He grew taller than all his brothers and developed a deeper voice during puberty.

Stew, Max, and Mell had cut off their braids and had growth spurts, too.

King and Frank weren't so lucky, having received their height from Momma's side of the family they was short.

"Happy B-day, lil' bra!" King said as he dapped up Tony and hugged him.

"Good lookin', bra. Stay yo lil' ass out of jail," Tony replied, joking because he was towering over him.

King laughed. "Shut up, nigga. I don't care how big you get, I still will whoop yo' ass."

Max and Chris crept up behind Tony. "Come on, y'all! We got him!" They grabbed both of Tony's arms. Stew, Mell, Frank, and Reggie ran up and gave him sixteen birthday licks. Tony laughed and tussled with his brother's trying to break loose. Momma stood on the back patio looking at her kids.

"My boys aren't boys anymore," she thought to herself. She started reminiscing about the old days when they were younger and how they scrambled around the house on Sunday mornings, arguing and fighting each other before church. Being stared at when she walked into service with all her boys every Sunday morning. And she thought about all the pessimistic letters Stan wrote to her, and how the boys stuck together through all the adversities throughout their childhood.

"God, you are sooo good," she said, smiling and shaking her head.

Uncle Bunky walked outside onto his patio wearing a two-piece silk Versace pajamas set. The top was unbuttoned, exposing his chest hair. Only on special occasions did he step outside. His usual was to chill in his man cave, smoke weed, and watch sports.

"Happy birthday, knucklehead," Uncle Bunky said, leaning over the patio with his elbows on the banister.

"Thanks, Unc," Tony said.

"You still playing ball?" Uncle Bunky asked as he inhaled his reefer.

"Yeah, I play for Shaw now!" Tony replied fanning the smoke out his face.

"That's right, my baby's in high school now!" Momma said.

Uncle Bunky turned and looked at Momma. "Mind yo' business! Ain't nobody ask you."

Momma laughed. "Shut up, that's my baby!" she said sitting on the patio porch swing.

"Baby boy!" Uncle Reggie called Tony over to the grill.

"What's up, Uncle Reggie?" Tony walked over and grabbed a hotdog from the aluminum pan. He stuffed a big bite in his mouth.

"Run to my van and grab that bag off the passenger seat."

"Alright," Tony said walking away. He got to the car, grabbed the small bag out of his van and ran back to the backyard.

"Here, Uncle Reggie," Tony said, handing him the small bag.

"Happy birthday, boy," he said, letting Tony know the bag belonged to him.

"Oh, snap! This mine?" Tony asked as he ripped open the bag.

Uncle Reggie smiled. "Yeah, that's for you, baby boy."

Tony pulled the 24K gold watch out of the bag and twirled it around, blissfully examining it before putting it on his wrist.

"Good lookin', Uncle Reggie! This raw!" Tony ran and showed it off to everybody.

Frank and Pierre sat at the spades table with Chris and Lippy playing Cutthroat.

"Y'all going' to that kickback tomorrow night?" Chris asked.

"Who, that girl Tierra kickback?" Frank asked.

"Oh yeah, I heard about that shit," Pierre said.

"Yeah, I heard it was gon' be some bitches there," Frank said.

"Hell, yeah! We there," Chris said, nodding his head.

Frank, Pierre, and Chris were in the eleventh grade at Shaw High, where Tony had already filled his big brother's shoes as a freshman. He had become a high school phenom.

On game nights, Tony put on a provocative show. Every home game the whole city came out to watch him play, from the dope boys on the corners to the teachers in schools. His primary position was linebacker, but due to the team's lack of talent, he ended up playing multiple positions on both sides of the ball.

All of Kim's boys slowly began to grow more and more into the streets as they got older, except for Tony; his focus was football and only football. Tony really had a mind of his own, no matter what he saw going on around him he stayed focused on what he loved.

Max and Lil' Chuck grew tight. They ran together like Batman and Robin, all day, every day.

Then one day, Lil' Chuck got ahold of his stepfather's .40 caliber and ran around East Cleveland treating it like a paintball gun. Shooting up anything in his sights. One of the bullets hit a man in the leg. He later died from the wound.

Lil' Chuck went on the run, but ended up turning himself in after the police arrested his family. He was sentenced to thirteen years in prison for involuntary manslaughter.

After Stew's career was shattered, he felt his only option was to go back to the streets.

"Ain't nobody 'bout to hire me. I'm Black with felonies and a weak ass East Cleveland education," were the thoughts that went through his mind whenever he thought about finding a job.

During Stew's five-year bid in juvie, he met Lippy, who was paralyzed from the waist down. He'd been sentenced to juvie life for conveying bricks of dope. He was released two months before Stew, and Stew protected him like a brother during their bid. They utilized their time politicking and strategizing on how to come home and get money.

Chapter Eleven

"Tony get up, you ain't coming with us?" Pierre said as him and Frank got dressed for the kickback.

"Naw. I got practice in the morning," Tony said laying in his bed. Frank and Pierre was on Frank's side of the bedroom putting on their best clothes to impress girls at the kickback.

"Aye Tony, let me wear dis," Frank asked as he held up Tony's new watch Uncle Reggie had gotten him for his birthday.

"Naw! Give me my stuff. You trippin'." Tony jumped up and snatched his watch out Frank's hand.

"Nigga don't snatch shit from me." Frank swung and hit Tony on the chin, Tony bull rushed Frank to the ground.

"Chill man! What the fuck y'all niggas doin'?" Pierre jumped between them breaking them up. "Y'all trippin'. Y'all gon' wake G'Momma up"

Tony got up and took his watch downstairs in the living room. Frank got up off the floor.

"Man where this nigga Chris at?" Pierre asked.

"I don't know, man that nigga always takin his sweet time," Frank said straightening out his shirt. Pierre and Frank had been waiting on Chris to get there so they could all go to the kickback together. "What's up, Tony?" Chris said walking in the house giving Tony some dap.

"Aye Frank, Pierre, y'all ready?" Chris yelled from the living room.

"You jus' talked him up," Frank said. They ran down stairs into the living room.

"Damnnnn my nigga, that's how you feel?" Frank smiled and dapped Chris up.

Chris drew a huge smile from ear to ear and said, "What you mean?"

"Aw hell naw! I ain't goin'," Pierre said. He saw how fresh Chris was and figured nobody would pay him no attention at the kickback because his outfit wasn't up to par.

"What you mean you ain't goin'? What y'all talkin' about?" Chris said smiling chewing on some Winterfresh.

"Nigga you walked in here lookin' like Diddy, and we look like we jus' paid a dollar for dress down day," Pierre said.

Tony laid across the couch laughing at Pierre.

"Man, shut up, nigga" Chris said smiling. He handed them both a piece of gum, and headed out the door.

"Come on, we out y'all" Chris said.

They all dapped Tony up before they left out to the kickback. Tony laid across the couch and watched TV until he fell asleep.

Max, Stew, and Lippy was chillin' in the Sunnyspot.

The Sunnyspot was their everyday chill spot. The owner and security guards was close to all Momma's boys since they were kids. They were treated like family anytime they entered the place.

Stew was sitting at the bar having drinks. It was a descent night with a nice crowd. A pretty, high yellow chick came and sat next to him.

"How you doing? I'm Stew," he said extending his hand at the redhead woman.

"I'm fine," she responded sounding dry and uninterested with no eye contact.

"Can I buy you a drink?"

"That's okay honey, I'm fine," she replied.

Stew looked at the bartender and signaled for two doubles of Patron, then turned his attention back to the woman sitting next to him.

"Seems like you had a long day," Stew said.

She didn't reply. She was irritated. She'd just gotten into a fight with her baby daddy. She just wanted to get away for a second. After a few doubles of Patron, she began to open up.

"Ohhhh! This my song," she through her hands in the air snapping her fingers.

Mitch caught a body 'bout a week agoooo... she sang the lyrics to Bobby Shmurda's song as it thumped through the speakers.

"Man, I can't do that dance for shit," Stew said laughing as he tossed back his fourth double of Patron.

"Come on. Come on," she said. "I'ma teach you." She grabbed Stew's arm and pulled him on the dance floor. The Patron was in full effect.

Lippy was on his phone texting. Max stood behind his wheelchair when he noticed a familiar face walk through the doors of the bar. The man looked angry and like he was up to no good.

The man scanned the bar and noticed his baby momma on the dance floor with Stew. The girl's baby daddy pulled out a small pocketknife from his grey Polo joggers, pulled his hood over his head, and headed straight towards the dance floor. His adrenaline rushed as he quickly maneuvered his 6'4" frame through the crowd towards the dance floor. Max rolled Lippy's chair to the side as he locked his eyes on the man.

"Bitch, what the fuck is wrong with you?" He yolked her up by her neck.

"Aye man, don't be putting yo' hands on a female like dat?" Stew said as he stepped up into her boyfriend's face.

Baby Daddy bit down on his bottom lip, and swung his blade at Stew's chest barely grazing his skin, but slicing a hole into his white t-shirt. Stew jumped back and threw his guards up.

Baby Mama screamed and ran behind Stew, grabbing a tight grip on the back of his shirt, afraid for her life. Max came flying through the crowd with an empty Corona bottle.

"Watch out, nigga," Max yelled as he shattered the bottle across the back of his head.

Two security guards rushed the man to the ground, pounded him out on the dance floor, and then started dragging Baby Daddy toward the exit. He wiggled out from the security's possession, broke loose and ran to his black Chevy Tahoe in the parking lot behind the bar. He popped open the hood and grabbed his loaded 9mm he had tucked by the engine.

Then Baby Daddy changed out of his hoodie and walked back to the front of the bar at a fast pace. As he approached the front of the bar, he spotted Max, Lippy, and Stew pulling off in Lippy's '74 Cutlass. He immediately ran back to the parking lot, jumped in his truck, and skirted out the lot to follow them. But, by the time he got back to the front of the bar, they were gone.

Stew reclined his seat as they drove down the street. "Man, that nigga looked familiar," he said as she leaned back and looked at Max in the backseat.

"Yup," Max said, sitting in the back seat in deep thought, trying to remember where he recognized his face from.

Max was the type who never did much talking when he was mad. Lippy turned his music up and continued cruising down Euclid as 50 Cents *Many Men* thumped through the speakers.

Pierre, Frank, and Chris returned from the kickback and passed out on the floor in the TV room. Pierre and Frank knocked off two pretty, light skin girls at the kickback and ranked on Chris the entire walk home for being so fresh and not getting any girls' phone numbers.

Tony stretched his 6'2" frame across the living room couch with the window slightly cracked by his head to catch a breeze. He was knocked out, when suddenly he heard loud screeching brakes outside of the house. Half sleep, he took the blanket off, lifted his head and peaked open one eye to look out the window and saw a black Tahoe with its park lights on sitting in the front of the house. He noticed a man running towards the porch pointing something at the house.

He threw the blanket back over his head and shut his eyes.

"*Pow! Pow! Pow! Pow! Pow! Pow! Pow!*" Seven shots came through the house. Bullets shattering through the windows. It was nonstop ringing.

Tony curled up in a ball with his hands on his head. Eyes shut tight waiting for the shooting to stop. He looked up and saw bullet holes in the couch inches from where his head had just been.

The man ran off the porch, jumped in his truck, and skirted off up the street. The neighbors heard the gunshots and called the East Cleveland police.

Four a.m., multiple police cruisers were parked at Momma's house. The red and blue police lights lit the neighborhood up like it was an amusement park. After years of chaos and violence, Momma's house became a regular routine stop for East Cleveland police officers.

Detective Nikki Jones had been working on the force for East Cleveland for over fifteen years. Her son, Deandre aka DJ, went to school and played football with Tony from mini league middle school to high school.

Tony and DJ became close friends and mostly hung out a lot at school. Detective Nikki grew a liking to Momma after years and years of watching her fight through each deep emotional situation that came upon her. She took Momma out for lunch and drinks from time to time.

Momma called Uncle Reggie after the incident. He jumped out the bed and flew over to Momma's. He walked into the house and saw Tony with that same look he had when the incident occurred years ago. The one after his mini league football game in Uncle Reggie's Astro van when those dudes tried to rob him.

Seeing his life flash before his eyes had made him look at life in a different perspective. His eyes got watery as he sat on the living room couch, hunched over, resting his elbows on his knees. He looked around at the scene—seeing broken glass scattered on the floor, staring at Momma with multiple officers in her face really began to take a toll on him. The only thing he could look forward to that would take some stress away was practice in a few hours.

After the police left, Uncle Reggie gave Tony a small pep talk right before him and Frank went into their room and fell asleep. The incident that happened the night before at Tony's house spread through Shaw High like the chickenpox. Everyone heard about his house being shot up and there were all types of rumors going around like his dad broke out of jail and was the one who did it. People was even saying one of the bullets grazed Tony's head.

Tony and his friend DJ, Detective Nikki Jones' son, sat in the lunchroom at the senior table together alone talking.

DJ was a short, dark skin guy with little dreads. He was the type of dude that didn't bite his tongue for anything. If he felt something wasn't right, he spoke on it bluntly. Then a group of pretty girls from the cheerleading team came up asking about the incident from the night before.

"Hey, Tony. Are you okay?"

"Yeah, I'm good," Tony said, he hugged a few girls, thanking them for their concern.

DJ sat back and looked at the girls surrounding Tony. DJ hated when he felt people was showing fake love and fake smiling faces.

"Is your mom and brothers and everyone alright?" the girls asked.

"Yeah he alright damn, Can't you see he walkin' and talkin'? Damn, y'all actin like some groupies," DJ yelled as he slammed his hand on the table.

"Boy, bye! I ain't never no groupie," one of the cheerleaders said as she jumped in his face.

'Bitch, you better get back 'fore I slap that cheap-ass wig off yo' head."

"Man, sit down. You bet not think about puttin' yo' hands on no girl." Tony stepped in between DJ and the girls.

"Man, I'm out," DJ said as he turned around and walked out the lunchroom. DJ was secretly jealous of Tony, but Tony was blinded by it because of his loyalty.

"Hey Ms. Smith," Tony said as he walked into math class late.

"Tony this is the fifth time this week you've been late to my class. The next time you're late, I'm gonna give your mom a call."

"You might as well call her now so I can get my whoopin' on and out the way," Tony said being a class clown.

"Okay, you want to be funny, come up to my desk," the teacher said picking up the schools' telephone on her desk.

Tony walked up to the teacher's desk.

"What is your mom's phone number?" Ms. Smith asked.

Tony wrote the number on a scrap piece of paper and walked to the back of the classroom as she dialed it.

"Hi. This is Ms. Smith at Shaw High School."

"Oh, hey. How you doin?"

"I'm calling in regarding to Tony's tardiness to class this week. The whole classroom was giggling as the teacher continued talking on the phone.

Tony had given his teacher his own cellphone number and walked to the back of the classroom pretending to be his mother. Everybody noticed what he'd done when they saw him in the back of the classroom covering his mouth with his hand disguising his voice.

Everyone but the teacher.

Chapter Twelve

After a long day of school with a bunch of people in his face all day asking questions about the night before, Tony couldn't wait to hit the field. The field was his only way to get peace of mind and let off some steam.

"Let's go, Tony!" Coach Brown yelled as Tony knocked the running back off his feet and flat on his back during their scrimmage.

Coach Brown was the head coach of Shaw High School where Tony attended. And other than Coach Rick and Uncle Reggie, he was another father figure who played a strong role in his life.

Coach Brown was a huge dark-skinned man with wavy grey and black peppered-colored hair. He had a great personality off the field, the funniest football coach you would ever meet. But he didn't play nor joke come game time. He pushed Tony to levels Tony didn't think he could reach.

"Good work today, boy." Coach Brown slapped Tony on the helmet as he ran onto the sideline.

"Yup!" Tony replied as he grabbed a water jug and squeezed the water into his mouth through the holes in his facemask. They walked toward the locker room after practice.

"Aye, coach," he said, taking off his helmet.

"What's on your mind, Tony?" Coach Brown asked, seeing Tony's frustrating demeanor.

The locker room was dark. Only one light worked and a majority of the lockers were broken. The rest of the players were scattered around talking and changing out of their practice gear. Tony sat down on the floor and leaned against the lockers.

"What if I don't score high enough on my SAT?" he asked, looking up at Coach Brown standing over him.

Tony had been worried about his scores for weeks. Now, that it was close to the time that the results for his test were coming back, he began to get worried.

"Don't worry about that right now. Just focus on football. You already took the test, and you gave your best shot. That's all that matters."

"If I don't score high enough, I won't be eligible to play D1?" Tony asked with his elbows on his knees, sitting against the locker and looking up at Coach Brown.

"If push comes to shove, you'll have to play a year in junior college."

"That's all I need. Just put me on that field, and I'ma take it from there," he said as he extended his arm up for Coach Brown to help him up off the locker room floor.

Coach Brown pulled him up to his feet, rested his hand on Tony's shoulder, and looked into his eyes. "Tony, no matter what college you go to, you're gonna be great. Just stay in school and give it everything you got and don't come back here. I've watched too many of my boys get inches away from making it and fail right before they get a shot at their dream. And one of them boys was..."

"My brother. I know," Tony said, cutting him off.

"Yes, Stew. And we're not about to let that happen to you."

Tony walked in the house after a long day of school and practice.

"Hey, Momma. What you doing?" he said as he tossed his gym bag in the closet and gave Momma a hug. She was sitting at the dining room table reading mail.

"Hey, my baby. How was school?" Momma asked.

He smiled as he held his hands behind his back, hiding something from Momma.

"Boy, what you got behind yo' back?" Momma asked, trying to peak around him.

"Wait, Momma. Close yo' eyes," Tony said.

He stood behind Momma while she sat in the chair. He pulled out the paper.

"BAM! Third week in a row," he said as he slammed the article on the table.

"You made it again!" she shouted, smiling.

She jumped up and squeezed him tight. Tony made the Plain Dealer's player of the week three weeks in a row. Momma knew how hard Tony worked and loved to see him get acknowledged or rewarded for it. Monday through Friday, it was school and practice, and Saturday mornings he ran four miles at the park up the street from Momma's house.

Mell, Stew, and the rest of the boys came downstairs when they heard Momma screaming.

"What happened?" Max, Frank, and Stew asked in unison.

Momma held up the newspaper article. "He did it again!" Momma shouted. "Tony made player of the week again!"

"Ahhhhh," they all chanted in celebration.

"Yeahhhh, bruh, that's what I'm talkin' about." All his brothers yelled the words and surrounded him, congratulating him.

After a few moments, the room cleared and Tony sat down at the table alone, thinking about his SAT scores.

I gotta score high enough on this test. I can't let Momma down. Thoughts ran wild in Tony's head.

Tony dropped his forehead, he lifted his head and saw the letter on the table from Stan that Momma was reading. He opened the letter and immediately began to tear up with the first three sentences. As he began to read, frustration built up inside of him.

Listen, like I told you before, you dumb bitch, you gonna end up dead. Your house out there getting shot up. and I told you those lil' niggas aint gon' be shit. I told you, you can't raise them by yo'self. You need me, you stupid motherfucker. You need to go somewhere and stimulate yo' mind. Hit a pipe and get yo' head together. You was smarter when you did that. You just dumb now. And by the way, stop lying to Tony. Tell him the truth I'm not his father. Tell the lil' motherfucker who his real father is.

Tony couldn't continue to read. He put the letter down as tears of anger built in his eyes. The only man he knew was Stan since a child. He wouldn't had ever thought to believe that Stan wasn't his biological father.

"Seventeen years," he said softly to himself. Seventeen years I thought he was. If he ain't, who his?

Frank walked back into the dining room and saw Tony sitting at the table alone.

"What's up, bruh? What's wrong with you?" Frank asked.

"Man, look at this," Tony said as he slid the letter across to Frank.

Frank read the letter and looked up at Tony as he sat at the other end of the table with tears of anger in his face. He didn't want to let Momma know he read the letter, so he stood up from the table, walked outside onto the front porch and called Uncle Reggie.

He paced back and forth on the porch with his phone to his ear. The phone rang and constantly went to voicemail, which was unusual. Uncle Reggie never missed phone calls from Tony or Momma.

Tony slipped his cellphone in his basketball shorts and sat down on the front porch stairs. Daydreaming about playing in the NFL, and buying Momma a huge house with a Mercedes Benz in the driveway.

Tony's phone rang, snapping him out of the daydream. Uncle Reggie was calling him back. Tony flipped open his phone.

"Hello?"

"What's up, baby boy?" Uncle Reggie mumbled in a low, soft, raspy voice.

"Sorry Unc, I didn't mean to wake you up," Tony said, noticing the tiredness in his voice. "I can call you back later when you wake up."

But Uncle Reggie wasn't sleep. He was on bed rest in the hospital after being diagnosed with cancer. He only had two months left to live and didn't know how to break the news to anyone, especially not Tony.

"Naw, it's okay, baby boy. Talk to me. What's on yo mind?" he said in a low raspy whisper.

Tony explained to Uncle Reggie about the letter Stan wrote Momma from prison. Tony went on and on until Uncle Reggie cut him off.

"Tony, listen to me. There's something I call tunnel vision where you close your eyes and put yourself in a dark tunnel. This dark tunnel in your mind is how you live your life, with just you and your goal at the end of it. Remember, the most important part about this tunnel is that no one is in it but you, and the goal is to reach the light at the end."

Tony closed his eyes as Uncle Reggie continued to explain the tunnel vision to him.

"A good thing to do is put something that will entice you to strive and go hard as possible at the end of your tunnel."

Tony immediately painted a picture of Momma's smile and put it at the end of his tunnel right beside a big, bright NFL logo that glowed bright.

"Keep in mind everything outside of your tunnel isn't important. So, you never want to come out. Once you're deep enough in your tunnel, only one thing should matter to you, and that's reaching the end of it. Nothing else matters. Nobody's opinion, what anybody thinks or says, nothing.

"Negativity is gonna try to finesse its way into your tunnel all the time, but you can't let it. But even if somehow the negative make its way in, sometime you have to embrace it because you can learn from those moments. When things don't go as planned, it's always a detour. Remember that. The only way you'll lose is if you stop."

Tony listened to Uncle Reggie. As he spoke, Tony visualized himself inside his tunnel.

"When those barriers come, you got two options: knock them down or let them knock you down."

"I ain't letting nothin' knock me down Unc," Tony said.

"That's right. Take it personal," Uncle Reggie replied.

Tony hung up the phone. Momma called him upstairs and broke some unexpected news to him.

"Sit down," Momma said as she laid across her queen-size mattress.

Tony sat on the edge of Momma's bed and looked at her unfolding some papers.

"Your SAT scores didn't come back high enough."

"You serious?" he said as he looked into Momma's eyes.

"Yes, baby. The school just called and told me."

Tony sat at the edge of Momma's bed, took in a deep breath and exhaled. "It's cool. I'ma talk to

Coach Brown and see what I need to do next," he said.

Momma was stunned by his reaction. She knew how desperate Tony was for positive results, and she really was just as anxious as he was.

I ain't about to let this stop me, Tony thought to himself thinking about what Uncle Reggie had just told him.

Chapter Thirteen

Frank was running home as fast as he could, the light drizzle of the rain slapping his face. He sprinted down the street toward the house. He couldn't wait to get home and tell Tony what he'd just found out. He bust through the front door.

"Bruh, I gotta show you something important. Come upstairs," he said to Tony as he flew past the living room.

He noticed Tony didn't move. Frank stopped and walked backwards to the living room and saw Tony's face soaking wet and his eyes bloodshot red.

"What happened, bruh? You a'ight?" Frank asked as he sat down next to Tony.

Tony shook his head side to side, staring at the floor.

Stew and Max walked in the house and saw Frank and Tony and sat with them. They already assumed they knew what the issue was. Stew and Max put their hands on Tony's shoulders for comfort.

"It's cool, Tony. Uncle Reggie's with God now," Stew said as he hugged his lil' brothers.

"What happened to Uncle Reggie?" Frank asked, unaware.

Max sat next to Frank to put his arm around him. "He got sick. They found cancer in his lungs," Max replied.

"Man, what!" Frank said. He dropped his head as tears fell down. He looked up at Tony and saw nothing but pain in his eyes as a tear slowly rolled down his cheek as he made a tight fist.

The room was quiet as the four of them had their heads down before Tony broke into an outburst.

"Nooooo, not Uncle Reggie! Not Uncle Reggie! What I'ma do now? What I'ma do without my uncle, man!" Tony dropped to his knees screaming.

"Bruh, he's still wit' us," Stew said as he helped lift Tony off the floor. "He just' gone physically, but his spirit is wit' us forever," Frank said.

Tony just shook his head side to side.

Stew put his hand on the top of Tony's head.

"We all we got, lil' bra. We gotta stay strong for each other and Momma. Plus, we got an angel watching over us. Uncle Reggie is still wit' us, and he probably cussing you out right now for cryin' like this," Stew said.

Max squatted down in Tony's face. "Wipe yo' face, lil' nigga, 'fore I give you something to cry about," Max said, mocking Uncle Reggie, impersonating his voice.

Tony grew a small smirk on his face.

"Mannnn, you sounded just like him," Tony laughed.

The four of them sat in the living room reminiscing about Uncle Reggie for hours. Then Max and Stew went out to ride through the streets with Lippy in his old school Cutlass. Tony and Frank was chilling in the living room while Momma was at work.

"Aye, bruh. What you have to show me?" Tony asked Frank.

"Look at this," Frank said as he pulled out a piece of paper and showed it to Tony.

"Man, whatttt," Tony said with a jaw-dropping look. "You got a baby?" he asked, surprised.

"Yeah, bruh. 99.9%. She had him two days ago," Frank said, he looked Tony in his eyes. "I don't know how I'm gonna raise him. I don't know how to raise no baby. I could see if we had a dad I could get some advice from or some shit."

"Bruh, you gonna be good. Just make sure you stay in his life. That's all he needs."

"Oh yeah, I'ma do that fa'sho," Frank replied.

Frank had a boy. They named him Naz, after his favorite rapper. Within a few months, Frank built the strongest bond a father could have built with his child. He and his son were inseparable. Their bond was unbreakable. He never left his side.

Tony became really attached to Naz, too.

Chapter Fourteen

Coach Rick, Coach Brown, Quana, and Momma all stood in the stance screaming and chanting Tony's name.

"Let's give a round of applause for our 2011 graduates!"

The auditorium roared so loud you felt the rumble in your feet. Tony sat in the chair in his cap and gown next to Tamika, a girl who he had a crush on, waiting on his name to be called.

Tamika was a dark skin pretty girl with the perfect shape and long hair. She used to walk around the school with her nose up. She knew she was the prettiest girl in school, and she took full advantage of it with her arrogant attitude. Tony wanted her bad, but he just knew she would turn him down.

"What's up Tamika," Tony said looking over at her.

"Hey," she said looking into Tony's eye. Tony was surprised she even spoke back. That gave him more confidence to keep flirting.

"What you doin' after the graduation?"

"Boy I know you ain't tryna flirt wit' me?" she said with a nasty attitude throwing her head back.

"I would never in a day be seen with you" She said shutting Tony's hopes down. Tony didn't respond, he turned back towards the stage waiting on his name to be called.

Momma looked at her baby in his cap and gown waiting to walk across the big stage. She smiled as tears of joy fell down her face. She couldn't believe her baby was all grown up and graduating from high school. The Cleveland State Wolstein Center was packed from the nosebleeds to the floor as the students were beginning the next chapter of their life.

"I'm so proud of you, Momma," Coach Brown said. He hugged Momma. They rocked from side to side as she cried.

"He's gonna be great," Coach Rick whispered in her ear as he gave Momma a hug.

"Yes, he is," Momma said.

While Tony sat in the chair waiting on his name to be called, Momma was reminiscing with Coach Brown, Coach Rick and everybody else about Tony.

"Let me tell y'all something about him. Tony's the wrong person you wanna try to rank on. I'm tellin' you don't do it. I remember one day after practice, the whole damn team was in the locker room, and I made the dumbest mistake talkin' about how big his head was. First, he said I look like the dad from *Meet the Browns*. Then he took it to a whole 'nother level and said I look like a dick wit' ears. When I tell you he tore my ass up! I mean tore my ass up! That muthafucka had me walkin' to my car 'bout to cry. He humiliated me in front of my whole damn team. I had to apologize after that day."

Everybody laughed.

"What about him wrestling his last year? Who gave him that idea?" Momma sarcastically asked, looking at Coach Brown.

"I didn't tell him to wrestle. I told that boy to run track. He came to me one day and said he was signing up from wrestling," Coach Brown said.

After playing football his entire childhood, he wanted to do something new and different. So, Tony wrestled for his high school during his senior year.

His first time wrestling he went undefeated. He made the Plain Dealer Player of the Week for wrestling and won 1st place gold in every wrestling tournament all while he was committed to a junior college in Kansas. He went to Columbus for the state championships and went undefeated in that tournament, and with one man to beat to become the state champion, he lost by a point.

"One thing I love about him is his confidence," Coach Rick said. "Whatever he does, he takes control and does it with confidence."

"Yup, that's my baby." Momma smiled and gave Coach Rick a high-five.

Frank, Pierre, Chris and DJ went wild when the man called Tony's name to receive his diploma.

"Roof, roof, roof!" Coach Brown chanted as he pumped his fist in the air.

After the ceremony, everybody went to Momma's house. Quana cooked her specialty: macaroni & cheese, yams, greens, and ham, with cheesecake for dessert.

A couple weeks later, Tony left to Kansas for school. Momma, Frank, Chris, and Coach Brown took him to the airport.

"I love you, bruh. Call me when you land," Frank and Chris said as Tony grabbed his luggage from the trunk.

"A'ight, bet. I love y'all, too," Tony said back.

Momma hugged Tony for a long time. Tony looked at Momma, grabbed her hand and said, "Momma, you're my motivation. I love you, and I promise I'm going to get you out of that city one day."

"Tony, don't you worry about me. You just make sure you go to church down there and keep your grades right. That's how you make me happy." She squeezed him tight before he walked away.

Momma, Frank, Pierre, and Chris stood and watched as Tony walked away to board his flight to Kansas.

Tony didn't know what college would be like. He had no clue how college was, how the lifestyle was, or how people would treat him there. Before the flight took off, he quickly Googled Kansas University. He saw the beautiful college scene, the huge campus, and all the students having a blast. He couldn't wait to arrive to his new school, and more importantly, hit the field.

As the flight took off, he looked out the window and took a final glance at the city. Then a feeling like no other came over him. A strong chill came through his flesh.

"Tony knew that feeling was Uncle Reggie reminding him that he was with him. The last words Tony heard from Uncle Reggie was, "It's personal."

Tony dozed off and began dreaming about living an abundant life with Momma and his brothers on an island in Puerto Rico.

"Excuse me, sir. Sir!" the flight attendant said as she tapped Tony, waking him up out of his sleep.

He got up, confused and discombobulated. *I'm here already,* he thought to himself as he got off the plane carrying his luggage.

When he arrived, he looked around as if he was in the middle of nowhere. He looked around and saw nothing but farms and tall grass everywhere. He jumped into the black Tahoe that was waiting for him outside the airport.

"Back from break?" the driver asked as he took off up the road heading towards Tony's school.

"Naw, I'm a freshman. This is my first year," Tony replied as he looked out the window at the cows and sheep and farmland.

He had his Beats headphones resting around his neck as he sat in the backseat on his way to junior college. When the driver pulled up to the school, Tony stepped out of the truck, threw his bag over his shoulder and looked around. *What the hell is this?* Tony thought to himself. This was not the place Tony thought he was coming to. He immediately jumped on the phone.

"Hello, Momma."

"Hey, baby. You made it?"

"Yeah, but this school ain't nothin' like I saw on them pictures. This place is smaller than Shaw. It looks like an elementary school, and it's in the middle of nowhere."

"It's okay, baby. Just go meet with the coach and talk to him you will be alright after you get settled in."

"Alright, Momma. I love you," he said as he hung up the phone.

He went inside the school and met with the head coach.

"There he is...the man of the year," the coach said with a heavy country down south accent.

"What's up, coach?" Tony said, smiling.

"How are you, my man?"

The coach gave him a tour around campus and his dorm room and introduced him to his roommate.

"Hey, Tony. This is Jerry. Jerry, this is your new roommate, Tony. He's a freshman linebacker from East Cleveland Ohio," the coach said.

Jerry was a big white boy about 6'5". He played offensive lineman, he had long hair and he was from Wichita, Kansas.

"What's up?" Tony said as he extended his hand for a handshake.

Jerry looked down at Tony's hand, turned around and walked into the kitchen.

"What's that about?" Tony said, scrunching his face looking at the coach.

"Oh, don't mind him. Jerry can act like an ass sometimes. Don't pay him any attention. Come on, let me show you the stadium," he said.

He led Tony through the campus, students stared and some pointed at Tony as he followed the coach to the stadium. A few students who followed college football recognized Tony from the newspapers and was excited to have him there. The campus was crowded it seemed as all the students happened to be outside this particular day.

"This is our stadium. This is where we'll be playing all of our home games," the coach said with his arms in the air as if he had entered paradise.

"Okay, okay," Tony said, nodding his head and looking around. However, he wasn't at all impressed with the bleachers and stadium without a skybox or scoreboard. His expectations were set much higher with college. He thought it would be much more than what it was.

Tony returned back to his dorm room. His roommate had a few of the other players from the team over playing a game. Tony walked in and saw his clothes pulled out of his bags and scattered all over the room.

"What the fuck!" he said, looking at the mess. He walked over and approached his roommate and three friends.

"Aye, who went through my bags?" he asked as he stood over them with his fists balled up.

Jerry turned around, looked at Tony with a smirk, and turned his back to him. The anger and tension that rapidly built inside of Tony gave him enough power to knock down a brick wall and flip over a semi-truck. He took a minute and thought about what was more important before he reacted.

Chapter Fifteen

After a few weeks of dominating in practice, the coaches gained an outrageous level of respect for Tony, but that only made certain players not like him as much. The head coach pulled him to the sideline one hot day after practice.

"Hey, Tony, I want to make you the team captain. I love your leadership," the coach said.

"Okay, coach," Tony said with a serious look on his face.

The blonde headed coach displayed a big smile as he grabbed his whistle hanging around his neck and blew it, getting all the players' attention.

"Alright, everybody, listen up!" he yelled with his heavy country accent. "This young man right here is now your new team captain."

Players began sucking their teeth and mumbling under their breath. Tony stood next to the coach holding his helmet under his armpit and chewing on the end of his mouthpiece.

After practice ended, Tony made a phone call home.

"Hey, Momma," Tony said with his phone to his ear.

"Hey, Tony. How you like it?" Momma asked in a dry tone.

"It's cool. What's wrong?" Tony asked, hearing his mother's tone.

"I'm okay," Momma replied.

"No, you're not, Momma. What's going on?"

Tony knew Momma would try to hold back telling him stuff just to keep him focused, but Tony hated when Momma did that, because he was always concerned about his family and felt he needed to know everything that went on.

"Pierre is in jail. They gave him five years," Momma said as tears fell down her cheeks.

"Jail?" Tony replied. "What happened?"

"Tony, I gotta call you back. I love you. Don't worry about nothin' here. You just focus on your school stuff," Momma said, rushing off the phone.

After that call, Tony's frustration level went up to one hundred. Tony went to his dorm and showered before he took a nap. Some of the college students hung around on campus while most of the athletes hung around the basketball court. Tony was knocked out in his bed snoring loudly while his roommate Jerry was on the other side of the room playing Madden on the Xbox with two of his boys.

"I dare you to smack him in the face with that chair," Jerry's friend said, smiling.

Jerry put the Xbox controller on the bed and smiled at his friend.

"Watch this," Jerry said as he stood up and picked up the chair. He folded the chair up, and the three of them tiptoed towards Tony's bed. Jerry and his friends were trying so hard to hold their laughs back as they walked up on Tony as he slept. Jerry lifted the chair behind his head, looking down at him. Tony's mouth was wide open snoring. Jerry's friend signaled with his hand, counting to three.

"1...2...3. WHAM!"

Jerry struck the chair across Tony's face and took off out the dorm and down the hall.

"Ahhhh, man! What the fuck!" Tony said as he got up, lightheaded and dizzy. Squinting his eyes, rubbing his head as a speed bump instantly grew. He jumped up and ran to the door.

Tony saw the backs of Jerry and two other dudes running down the hall laughing. That was it. Tony had reached his boiling point. He knew it couldn't be too many places they would run to with the campus being so small. He rushed out the dorm room and roamed around campus looking for Jerry.

Tony got so angry that tears began to build up. He stormed around campus searching for him for about ten minutes. Then he grabbed his iPhone and called home.

"Be quiet, y'all. This Tony on the phone. What's up, bruh?" Frank answered after telling Chris, Max, and Stew to quiet down so he could hear.

"Tell Tony I said what's up. Ask him do he need some money on his books," Max said.

Stew laughed. "Nigga, he ain't in jail. He in college."

Frank plugged his finger into his ear as he walked away from everyone so he could hear Tony.

"Man, I'm 'bouta get kicked out this school," Tony said.

"What you mean? What you talkin' about bra?" Frank replied.

After Tony told Frank about the incident, Frank was ready to book the next flight down to Kansas. Tony and his brothers were overprotective of each other.

"Bruh, just walk to the store or something. Do something to calm down."

"Man, ain't nothing around here. I'm in the middle of nowhere. It ain't nothin' but farms around here."

"Bruh, it's gonna start off hard. It's gonna get better. Just don't think about coming back home."

"Okay. I love you, bruh. I'll talk to you later," he said as he hung up.

Tony walked back up the long dirt road from the gas station. He was in basketball shorts and a wife beater, drinking a red Gatorade and eating a honey bun. Still frustrated, you could see the anger on his face.

He gotta come back to the dorm room. This nigga can't run forever, Tony thought to himself.

Walking towards the campus, he walked past the basketball court and spotted the roommate standing at the half court line talking to a few players from the team.

Jerry was like the ringleader. Everybody followed behind and intimated by him because of his size. Tony locked his eyes on him and walked to the basketball court. Students scattered everywhere. It was ninety degrees out, and nearly every student in the school was at the court.

Tony threw his Gatorade down and walked onto the court. He saw Tony walking towards him and laughed as he slapped his buddy on the back, pointing at Tony. Students saw Tony powerwalking towards the court and it immediately drew everyone's attention seeing the serious expression Tony had on his face.

"Which one of y'all hit me wit' dat chair?" Tony said walking up on the huge lineman.

He laughed and said, "What you gonna do about–"

Before he could finish his question, Tony delivered a haymaker to the right side of his jaw, instantly knocking him out cold. His huge frame hit the pavement hard. Tony kept punching him until students pulled him off.

"Keep trying me if y'all want to!" Tony yelled as he was walking away, heading back to his dorm room.

Nearly the whole school grew a liking to Tony after they found out he was so cool, funny, and fun to be around. He never got violent unless he was forced to protect himself. From that day forward, everywhere Tony went he drew a crowd because of his hilarious personality. All the girls wanted to be around him. He kept everybody laughing. Jerry approached Tony after practice in the locker room. The players on the team watched Jerry approach Tony for a rematch.

"Hey, Tony," Jerry said as he approached him.

The players in the locker room turned their attention on the two, ready to see a second round.

"I just wanna apologize to you. You're actually a good dude," he said as he extended his hand.

"It's all good, bruh," Tony said, he gave Jerry some dap. The rest of the players stared at the two waiting for another fight to happen. Everybody witnessed Tony and Jerry get cool and for the rest of the season the team grew tighter.

The weather was beautiful in Cleveland. Max and Lippy was out joyriding through the neighborhood showing off Lippy's '72 Cutlass with 24-inch Forgiato rims.

"There go them bitch-ass niggas that jumped me right there," the man said to his friend in the passenger seat.

"You sure dats them?"

"Yeah. I know dat muthafuckin' car," he said as he grabbed a bandana from the backseat and wrapped it around his face.

The girl from the bar abusive boyfriend finally caught up with them. He was searching for Lippy's old school Cutlass. That was the last time he saw them when they pulled off from the bar that night he caught his girl on the dance floor with Stew.

They were tailing Lippy and Max over the hill. On 152nd Street heading toward the intersection where a marathon gas station sat.

"Pull up on the side of them niggas. I got something for dey ass," he said as he cocked his loaded 9mm with an extended clip.

Lippy drove like a pro, using his paralyzed sticks to drive. He was floating through traffic. He went over the steep hill of the bridge as he rapped the lyrics to Lil' Cray's Kyrie Irving. "Shawdy, know dat I keep a pole everywhere I go, just know I got dat roll."

Max did an adlib. "Bitch, I got dat role on me, aye."

As him and Lippy sung, they both flicked their wrists out the sunroof as if they were shooting an imaginary basketball out the sunroof.

As they came to a stop at a red light, his Forgiato's continued to spin at the intersection while the music blasted through the speakers. People in the gas station at the intersection stared as Lippy's candy red old school grabbed attention from all over. Max sat in the passenger seat pumping his fist and nodding his head to the song.

Lippy glanced over and screamed, "Get down!" when he noticed the black truck on the side of them with a man hanging out the window wearing a black bandana tied around his face.

They let off fourteen shots nonstop. Lippy smashed the gas running through the red light. He immediately smashed into oncoming traffic, bringing his car to a complete stop. Max lifted his head to see what kind of truck the dudes were pulling off in.

"Oh shit! Get down!" Max yelled as he leaned over and shielded Lippy's entire body.

The man pulled his truck over, got out, jumped on top of Lippy's old school Cutlass, and standing on the hood let off fifteen more shots to finish Max and Lippy off. They jumped into the black Tahoe and skirted off.

Chapter Sixteen

After the season ended at his junior college in Kansas, Division 1 scholarships started pouring in from everywhere. Tony's performance was outstanding. The first few weeks Tony was very indecisive, he wanted to be as far away from home as possible which helped him narrow down his choices. After one visit to Arizona State, it won his heart over. He loved everything about it. The coaches, players, people, and the scenery. Everything was lit.

"It's so clean down here. You won't even find a piece of gum on the ground," Tony said to his new teammates as they walked through their college domains.

He built an unbreakable bond with a few of his teammates. They became his brothers. Also, the head defense coach, Coach Randolph, instantly became close to him after learning a little about his background and what he came from. With his educational background being so weak, they helped

Tony and worked overtime with him to comprehend and study plays from the playbook.

"We gotta get down to business, Tony. Our first game is in two months," his teammate Cherry, said to Tony as he scrolled through his phone.

Cherry was a big brown-skinned 6'6" defensive end with dreads from Florida with a heavy down south accent.

"I don't see why I need to learn all these plays, and my job is easy. All I gotta do is rush the quarterback," Tony said as him, Cherry and Coach Randolph sat at the table in the school library going over plays.

"Aye, boa, hol' up. Ain't this ya bruh?" Cherry said to Tony as he scrolled through Instagram.

Tony grabbed Cherry's phone and his heart immediately dropped when he saw the Instagram post about Max.

"WHAT THE..." Tony yelled as he held the phone inches away from his face.

He jumped up, ran out of the library and called home.

"Momma, what's going' on wit' my brother? Why everybody posting RIP Max on Instagram?" Tony asked, pacing back and forth outside the library on the school's campus.

Momma sat in a chair in the hospital next to Max.

"Everything's okay, baby," Momma replied as she wiped the tears away.

"Well, what happened? Why ain't nobody telling me nothing? Is he okay?" Tony asked.

"Hold on, baby," Momma said, putting Tony on hold as the female Asian doctor walked into the hospital room

"Ma'am, your son is a strong, brave young man."

"Umhmm," Momma said as she continued holding and rubbing Max's hand.

"If the paralyzed guy he was with had been hit by at least one of those bullets, he would have instantly passed away due to his health conditions, and it seems that your son was well aware of that the way he shielded him from getting hit by any bullets," the doctor said.

Momma shook her head side to side. "All glory to God," Momma cried repeatedly as she rocked back and forth in the chair.

"All glory to God." The doctor smiled and walked back out of the room.

"Hello? Hello Momma, what happened?" Tony said.

"He's fine," Momma replied.

"Somebody drove up on him and Lippy and started shooting. He was shot thirteen times, Tony, but by the grace of God, he is still here," Momma said, rubbing Max's hand as he laid in the hospital bed sleeping with clear tubes flowing oxygen through his nostrils.

"Thirteen times?" Tony repeated. "Where at? Who did it? What's going' on there?"

"Yes. In his head, stomach, arms, back, and chest. But, he's fine. He's sleep right now. When he wakes up, you can talk to him, just please don't be down there panicking just play football and focus on school baby," Momma pleaded.

"Okay, Momma I will. I love you," Tony said.

"I love you to my baby," Momma said before they hung up.

At practice the next day, Max was on Tony's mind extremely heavy. Every hit Tony made had an extra hundred pounds of pressure applied towards it. Every time he ran, he ran an extra mile and put an extra step in it. Every rep he did, he added an extra on. Tony was determined to continue to make his work ethic stronger and with every incident that happened back in Cleveland, it would make him work harder at achieving his goal.

The murder rate in Cleveland had grown over seventy-five percent from when Tony left home.

Tony hadn't talked to anybody in a while just to try and separate himself from the chaotic incidents and focus on his career. He called Frank one day after he had kept seeing posts on Instagram of different murders every day.

"What's going' on there, man," Tony said as he jogged around the track with his headphones in.

"Man, it's crazy, bruh. I need to get outta here," Frank replied in a low, depressing tone.

Tony stopped running when he noticed something didn't sound right about Frank. He knew Frank like the back of his hand, and he sensed something sounded different about him.

Breathing heavily, Tony responded,

"What's wrong wit' you, bruh?" He took a breath.

"Why you sound so down?"

"Nothin', bruh. I'm cool. I just...I just...never mind, man."

"You just what, bruh?" Tony asked drenched in sweat as the one-hundred-degree weather baked his skin.

Frank didn't respond He was silent as he sat in a closed dark abandoned garage. Sitting on a broken crate, tears slowly rolled down his cheek as he loaded a bullet into the gun.

"Hello...hello," Tony said, calling for Frank.

After about two minutes of silence, Frank answered.

"Yeah, bruh," Frank replied, dropping his head down. The tears fell harder and harder down Frank's face. His mind was racing a thousand miles per hour. So much negativity was going through his mind. It was killing him mentally. He wasn't himself. His mind was pessimistic. He felt that not being on earth would be more peaceful than living in this cold, dark world infested with fake people and fake love.

"What's wrong, bruh? Is Naz cool?" Tony asked.

Frank and his three-year-old son, Naz had an unbreakable bond. When Frank heard Tony say his son's name that instantly brought Frank back to reality. He looked at the gun and put it down.

"Yeah, he good, bruh," Frank said as he wiped his tears with the collar of his shirt and stood up off the broken crate.

"You know you can come down here whenever you need to just to get away from all that for a minute," Tony said.

Tony really began to fear for his family's life as the murder rates rose so quickly in Cleveland.

"Good lookin', bruh. I'ma come down as soon as I get everything situated here."

"Alright, bruh. I love you. I gotta finish working out, though. I'll talk to you tomorrow after practice."

"Alright, love you too bra," Frank said as he hung up the phone.

Frank sat back down on the crate and let his mind run wild. His anxiety and negative thoughts began to take over as he picked up the gun, cocked it and put it to his chest.

What's the point of living in this shit? This shit ain't fun. I'd be better off gone. What do I need to be here for?

Tears fell down harder and harder.

"Naw, naw, naw. I can't do dis, mannn," he said out loud to himself.

He quickly stopped his thoughts from running when a big image of his son's smile popped into his head. He picked up his phone and dialed his baby Momma's phone to hear his son's voice.

"Hello," she answered.

"W'sup? Where Naz at?" Frank said with his head resting on his forearm.

"Boy bye! Stop calling me while I'm at work," she said with a nasty tone, then hung up the phone in his ear.

Frank sat in the dark abandoned garage holding the phone to his ear listening to the disconnected beep sound after she banged in his ear. He picked up the gun and put it back to his chest.

Chapter Seventeen

September 5ᵗʰ. Game Day.

It was a big day for Tony. Not only was it his birthday, it was also the first game of the season. His first ever Division 1 college football game. Inside the locker room was turned to the max while the ASU players jumped around. The fans were pumped up getting ready for the players to come out the tunnel. The crowd went crazy, and the student section went even crazier an hour before the game started, Tony found out Ronald, one of his old teammates he played with for the Chiefs with was killed back in Cleveland.

Coach Randolph walked up to Tony in the locker room. "Boy, why you looking like yo' dog just' died. It's game day. Cheer up," he said as he slapped his helmet and began to jog out onto the field.

The drums and horns from the band, the feeling of the turf on the field, and the sound of the crowd was the best feeling he could ask for. Touching the field was his safe zone. All his problems went away any time he touched the field. Nothing else mattered but football.

The coach called Tony to the sideline for an audible. "Tony, bring it in."

Tony ran to the sideline.

"Yeah, Coach," Tony said as he stood in front of him.

"I need you to Audible drop into coverage instead of blitzing. I want you to watch the flats. Go! Go! Get out there," the coach said as he slapped Tony's helmet.

Tony was skipping backwards as he yelled, "I got you, coach."

He looked down and checked his shoes to make sure they were tied before he turned around and ran on to the field. At the snap, Tony lined up at the outside linebacker. He started to drop back but blitzed immediately when he saw the perfect opportunity to make a play. Running full speed, he rammed his helmet into the chest of the quarter, making the big sack. The crowd roared louder as his teammates celebrated on the big play.

"Yeahhhh, boi. Yeahhhh," Cherry yelled as he slapped Tony's helmet.

"Now that's what I'm talkin' 'bout."

Tony looked towards the sideline and saw his coach waving him in towards him. He sprinted to the sidelines smiling. His coach was hot as a firecracker. He went off with his country accent.

"What the hell is wrong with' you boy? You went against every damn thang I told you. I don't give a damn if you made a play. That's not the point. If I tell you what to do, you do it. Now get the hell off my field!" he yelled, pointing towards the bench.

Tony had never in his entire football career had anybody talk to him or coach him like this.

Who this dude think he talkin' to? Tony thought to himself as he went to the sideline with his head down. *Is this some shit they think I'm 'bouta get used to?*

Coach Randolph, the head defensive coach, approached Tony on the sideline. A black man with a buzz cut who sort of puts you in the mind of Denzel Washington.

"Tony, you made a big play. Don't worry about that. He's tough on everybody. He's just doing his job."

"Yeah, but I'm making good plays. What is he trippin' for? I feel like he got something against me or somethin'," Tony said with a confused look on his face.

"No, Tony. He has nothing against you. Trust me. That's just his style of coaching."

The referee blew the whistle.

"Alright, Tony, I gotta go," he said as he patted Tony on the back and ran onto the field to give the defense some tips during the timeout.

The head coach sat Tony out for the rest of the game. After the game in the locker room, Tony couldn't wait until the head coach was done talking to the team so he could approach him. ASU lost the game by a blowout. The coach stood in the middle of the players in the locker room talking.

"Terrible game today, I will see y'all tomorrow morning at six o'clock am to go over film."

They said a team prayer, and everyone ran to the showers. The coach approached Tony before he could say anything.

"Tony, I need to see you in my office tomorrow morning after film."

"Okay," Tony responded, giving him a serious look of assurance. He sat down in front of his locker stripping the spat from his cleats. His phone went off. He pulled it out and read a text from his high school friend DJ: *Stay strong, bro. I can't imagine what you going through right now. I know Frank was yo' boy. I hope he pull through.*

He dropped everything. His hands were shaking uncontrollably. *Please no. God, don't do this,* he said to himself as he tried to gain control of his hands from shaking to call Momma. He called and called, but Momma didn't answer. He began to panic. He called Stew who picked up on the first ring.

"What's up, bruh?" Stew said.

"What's wrong with' Frank?" Tony asked, nervously afraid to hear anything terrible.

He stood up and paced back and forth in the locker room, running his hand through his hair.

"He got shot in his shoulder. He cool doe," Stew said nonchalantly, smacking on some cheesy Cheetos potato chips.

"Where he at? Who did it? Why Momma ain't answering? What's going' on, bruh?" Tony asked his questions consecutively, not even giving Stew time to answer one of them. He began to feel lost and confused.

"I don't know, bruh. Frank told Momma he was at the wrong place at the wrong time, and he got caught in the crossfire of a shootout in East Cleveland. Momma's phone dead, but call Chris' phone. I think he's with Momma and Frank at the hospital," Stew said.

"Alright, bruh. Love you." Tony immediately hung up and dialed Chris' number.

"Tony, you okay?" Coach Randolph said as he walked up on him.

Tony held up his index finger with one hand and held the phone to his ear with the other as he called Chris' phone.

"What's up Tony," Chris answered, sitting across from Momma and Frank in the hospital.

"What's up? What happen?" Tony asked.

"He got shot... He was in the middle of a shootout."

While Chris talked to Tony on the phone, Momma stared at Frank laying in the hospital bed. She sat there listing to Chris tell Tony that story, but she knew something wasn't right and his story didn't add up. Her mother's instinct never lied to her. She could read the hurt all over her son's face. He was hurt, embarrassed, and most of all ashamed. Momma and Frank locked eyes. She grabbed Frank's hand as tears built up in her eyes.

She said, "You didn't have to do this."

Tears fell down Frank's face. He knew Momma knew he did this to himself.

"Here you go, Momma," Chris said, handing her the phone to talk to Tony.

"Hey, Momma, is he okay?" Tony asked.

"Yes, he's fine, Tony."

"I'm 'bout to fly home tomorrow. I need to see him and talk to him."

"No, Tony, you stay in school. He's gonna be fine."

"Okay, but this crazy," Tony said taking a deep breath. "I love you, Momma," he hung up the phone.

Coach Randolph walked up to him and put his hand on Tony's shoulder and said, "Whatever you do, just please don't go back there."

"This crazy, Coach. Every time I call home, I hear some bad news," Tony said looking at his coach.

"I know. You just need to focus on you. Focus on school and football."

When Coach Randolph said that, it reminded Tony of Uncle Reggie's tunnel vision conversation they had.

"You right, coach." Tony shook his head. "You right."

Tony decided to stay on course. The next morning he went and talked to the head coach. He found out that he wasn't as disappointed in him as he thought, the coach just wanted to make sure he learned to listen.

Chapter Eighteen

Frank and Chris began to fly to Arizona on a regular basis. Tony's teammates became so close to Frank and Chris, they became brothers. Every game they attended Tony's performance enhanced. After every big play he made, Tony would find Frank and Chris in the stands and point to them. Tony took all the negative news he'd been getting from home, and used it as motivation to go even harder when he did that His career began to take off like never before.

Tony's junior year was his breakout year and the beginning of things for him. The media, NCAA, and ESPN sports analysts said Tony's name regularly on TV.

Although the crime rate in Cleveland never eased up, Tony figured the only way to help was to turn the negative into a positive and become a role model for the people in his city.

He changed his social media name to, "4MyCityEC" which meant he was doing this for his city, East Cleveland, and he lived by one simple slogan—*it's Personal.*

Wrapped up in that single phrase he set out to define that the reason and motivation behind him playing football was personal. It was his way out.

And it showed.

"Three sacks, eleven tackles and a forced fumble. Outstanding performance out there tonight. Seems like you've gotten a boost of energy. Where did you find that?"

Tony stood in front of the reporter for a post-game interview. "My coaches and teammates always make it easy for me to execute," he said. "I can't take the credit for my performance without them."

"You're going into your senior year," the reporter said, "have you thought about entering the draft at all?"

He smiled and wiped the sweat off of his face before he answered. "I think about that every day I wake up, but it's one step at a time. I'm gonna enjoy this moment and embrace it. Hey, Mommaaaa!" Tony waved at the camera.

"Thank you. This is Kelly Davison reporting live from Tempe Arizona ESPN."

Tony ran off to the sideline to talk to one of his biggest fans, Ash.

Ash was a seven-year-old handicap child that Tony really connected with. After every game, Tony ran straight to Ash and gave him his game gloves, a hug, an autograph, and a picture.

The game was nationally televised, that meant everyone back home got to see it. Including Stan.

He was playing poker at a table with several inmates when he noticed Tony's face on the screen. He jumped up from the poker table.

"Ohhhh, shit, ya'll! That's my son. Turn it up! Turn it up!" he yelled, grabbing everybody's attention.

All the inmates crowded around the TV listening to his post-game interview.

"That's my boy," Stan said, slapping his chest. "That's my boy!"

One of the inmates blurted out, "That boy nice. He going' to the league for sure," as they showed the game highlights.

People always proud of you when you doing well, but Tony was doing it for himself. So that he could be the role model that boys like him needed.

He turned his work ethic up twenty times more as he saw the light at the end of the tunnel. He was going into his senior year and it was all or nothing. He knew he had to leave everything on the table.

Tony didn't go back home to Cleveland for nearly five years. Arizona became his new home. He said a prayer before he went to sleep every single night. Momma taught all of her boys to stay close to God no matter what situations came amongst them.

That was something Tony always remembered.

Dear Lord, thank you for everything you have done for me, and thank you for whatever you got planned for me in the future. Please keep my family safe and help the city get better and safer. God, I don't know where all these guns and shootings are coming from, but I know you got the power to stop it. Please watch over my brothers, family and friends. I love you so much, God. Amen.

Chapter Nineteen

Tony woke up the next morning at 5:45am before practice and listened to the news on the television like he did every morning while he got dressed.

He heard the news anchor say: *Fifty-two murder in 30 Days in the City of Cleveland.*

"Dang, man. That is crazy When is they gon' stop?" Tony said to himself. He shook his head and turned up the volume so he could hear it while he was brushing his teeth.

A police officer was gunned down last night on Cleveland's east side. Thirty-nine-year-old Detective Nikki Jones was a part of the force for over 15 years.

Tony dropped his toothbrush and ran to the TV.

"Whattttt!" He stood in front of the TV, staring with his jaw dropped. "I gotta call DJ," Tony said as he dialed his number.

He didn't get an answer. So, he sent a text to his phone, sending his condolences. Nikki Jones was the detective who from East Cleveland who grew to become one of Momma's friends, she was also DJ's mom.

What's up, bro? I can't imagine how you feel right now. I know words won't be able to come close to fixing this problem, but I want you to know I'm here for you, bro. You can call and talk to me about anything whenever I swear. I love you, bro.

Tony sent the message to DJ and went to practice.

"What's up? You a'ight, Tony? You look like yo' dog died," Coach Randolph said, walking into the locker room. Tony stood in front of his locker changing into his practice uniform.

"I'm good, coach," he replied.

He stuffed everything in his locker, put his shoulder pads, and helmet on before he went on to the practice field. While Tony was at practice, little did he know, a lot more was going on in East Cleveland

Around 10:00 a.m., Max and Mell, got into an argument about a pair of jeans. They was at Momma's house while she was at work. The argument quickly escalated once their pride and ego got involved. Soon it wasn't about the pants anymore.

"I will beat yo' ass," Mell said as he stood up and got in Max's face. They stood toe to toe.

"Do it then, bitch-ass nigga," Max shouted.

Frank and Chris jumped in between them.

"Man, y'all trippin'. It ain't even that deep."

Mell reached over Frank and Chris and punched Max in the jaw. Max couldn't defend himself. He was lightheaded and weak. He still had bullets inside of him that hadn't been removed from when he'd been shot. They tussled around the living room. Mell slung Max into the mantelpiece. He hit his head on the corner and fell to the ground halfway unconscious.

"Chill, Mell! You trippin'," Chris said.

"Yeah chill Nigga, this our brother. You tryna kill him," Frank screamed.

Max got off the floor and pointed at Mell.

"Come outside! I'm 'bouta buss yo' bitch ass," Max said as he limped out the front door on his wounded ankle rubbing his head.

"You ain't gonna do shit, nigga," Mell said as he walked towards the front door.

Max had a small .38 revolver in his pocket. He got from Lil' Chuck years ago. Max stood in the front yard with his hand gripped to the .38. He was nervous. Deep down, he was hoping Mell didn't really follow him outside because he would have to do it just to protect his pride.

"Chill, Mell! You trippin'." Frank said.

As Mell started to go outside behind Max, Chris and Frank ran and stood in front of the door blocking the exit. They tussled with Mell trying to get him to stay in the house and leave it alone. Max stood in the front yard looking at them tussle in the front doorway with his hand in his pocket. Mell broke through Frank and Chris and jumped over the front banister.

"Yeah. W'sup now!" Mell said.

Max pulled the revolver out, closed his eyes and pointed it at Mell's legs as he bit his bottom lip. He pulled the trigger. POW! He shot one time, dropped the gun and ran.

Mell fell to the ground screaming. Max had ran two houses down the street before he stopped and turned around. His conscious was eating him alive. Mell had a gunshot wound to his inner thigh, inches away from his testicles. Max turned around and ran back up the street and fell on top of Mell crying.

"I'm sorry! I'm sorry!" Max cried continuously.

"Ahhhhh! Get the fuck off me!" Mell said as he pushed Max off his leg.

Chris was stunned. He couldn't believe what he just saw. Frank ran in the house and called the ambulance as Max cried and cried in the grass on his knees next to his brother.

An ambulance came and took Mell to the hospital.

Chapter Twenty

"Man, is he serious?" Tony said to himself as he checked his phone after practice.

He had sixteen missed calls and five long messages from DJ. Tony stood in front of his locker with his equipment on reading DJ's messages.

My Momma got killed, and I can't even talk to nobody. I should never have to call you this many times. When all that shit happened wit' yo' brothers, I always called to make sure you cool. SMH! I see what's going on. You think you better than me.

Tony squinted at his phone with a, "WTF is he talking about?" look on his faced. He sent DJ a message back.

My fault bruh. I was at practice and I missed yo' calls. I'm sorry about yo' mom. Call me when...

Tony's phone rang, interrupting the text message he was sending to DJ.

"Hello." Tony answered his phone. It was Chris.

"Bra. Max shot Mell."

"What!" Tony slapped his hand across his forehead. "Is Mell alright?"

"Yeah. He good. He been in the hospital for some weeks, though. But he gon' make it."

"Is Max in jail?"

"No. No matter how many times the police questioned him, Mell never told them who did it."

"I can't take much more, man," Tony said.

"Yeah, me either. This crazy," Chris said. Then he hesitated. "Momma is in the hospital, too. She had a nervous breakdown after she found out about Mell."

"What the..." Tony shouted, he slammed his phone down and ran. He ran and ran and ran for miles across the city. This was the last straw. He couldn't take it anymore. He ran for hours until the sun went down.

"This is it...this is it," he repeated to himself. "Tunnel vision," he said as he ran the mountain.

Tony zoned East Cleveland completely out and focused strictly on what was in ahead of him, his last season, which would turn out to be his greatest year of his football career. He won back-to-back player of the week awards, led the nation in tackles for loss, became a leader of his team, and grew an even stronger bond with his teammates and Coach Randolph.

Tony wasn't going to let nothing get in his way of what he deserved. All while he was putting on the amazing performance as a senior, nobody in

Arizona knew all the problems he was dealing with. His way of dealing with them was using them as motivation to go even harder every day.

At the end of his senior year, Tony was invited to the All-American All-Star game in Florida. This was the perfect opportunity to bring the family together out of East Cleveland.

Momma, Quana, Mell, Max, Chris, Stew, Frank and his son Naz all flew out to Florida to see Tony play in his All-Star game. The family desperately needed that quick getaway. They spent a lot of time laughing and building memorable moments. Tony put on another outstanding performance for his family and fans. He made a sack after one play and pointed at the whole family they went crazy in the stands.

After the All-star weekend, Tony returned to Arizona to get back to business. It was time for the NFL Combine. It was getting close to the NFL draft, and the feeling in Tony's body was unexplainable.

"How did the All-star game go?" Coach Randolph asked Tony.

Tony was in the indoor practice stadium alone stretching and talking to Coach Randolph.

"It went good. I got a sack and three tackles."

"Did you have a good time with your family?"

"Yeah, coach." He paused and looked Coach Randolph in his eyes as he stretched his arm across his chest. "I'm glad they all came. I really missed them. I ain't saw my brothers in years."

"Didn't your brothers fly down here a few times?"

"Yeah, that was Frank and Chris. Only two of them. I got a lot more."

"That's real good. I'm glad y'all had a good time out there. Give you some time to clear your head."

Tony was so anxious for the NFL Combine and pro day to start. He had his mind set on running a 4.5 in the 40-yard dash and twenty-five reps on the bench press.

When Pro Day came, Tony had a nice performance with twenty-nine reps, and he ran a 4.6 in the 40-yard dash. Although he wasn't at all satisfied with his performance, that didn't stop NFL agents from calling.

Tony walked in his coach's office. "Aye, Coach Randolph."

"What's up, Tony?" Coach Randolph replied as he sat at his desk working on his MacBook.

"I'm going home for the draft. I wanna be wit' my family for this," Tony said.

Coach Randolph took his focus off of his MacBook and gave Tony a serious look into his eyes.

"I don't think it's a good idea. We can make some arrangements for them to come out here or something."

"My family is too big for all of them to fly out here. Ain't nothin' gon' happen. Everybody wanna see me make it in my city."

"It's too much of a risk, Tony the crime rate in that city right now is off the charts. I don't think it's worth it."

"I'ma be cool, coach. Trust me. I'ma be good." Tony patted Coach Randolph on his back and walked out his office. He boarded the next flight to Cleveland, Ohio.

Chapter Twenty-One

Momma planned a big draft dinner at the house for Tony. Tony hadn't seen his family and friends in years except for the trip in Florida. Everybody was at Momma's house for draft day when Tony walked in. He arrived at Momma's house at 8:30 p.m.

"TONYYYYYY!" everybody yelled as Tony walked through the door with an Arizona State cap and gear, holding his luggage and gym bag. He ducked down to avoid hitting his head on the entryway.

The feeling of being back in East Cleveland was an awkward feeling for him. It felt good to be around his family, but the city itself felt dark and depressing the second he landed into it. But, all those negative feelings went out the window when he walked in and saw his family.

"Uncle Tony, what's up?" Naz said as he reached his hand up to give Tony a high-five.

"What's up, big head?" Tony said as he snatched Naz off his feet and threw him in the air.

"Mommaaaaa!" he screamed putting Naz down. Tony gave Momma the longest hug he could give as he whispered in her ear, "This is it, Momma. It's all over. You ready for your new life?"

"Yes, my baby. Yes, I am," Momma replied as she squeezed Tony rocked side to side hugging.

"Alright Momma, let 'em go, Dang!" Stew said.

Momma laughed and slapped Stew on his shoulder. "Shut up, boy! I missed my baby."

The house was packed. Everybody was there. Even people Tony never saw before a day in his life.

It was Day 1, the first round. Tony's name didn't get called after the first four rounds passed. The house went from fifty people to his eight immediate family members. After the fifth and sixth round, he began to get worried as he looked over at Momma sitting next to him on the couch.

God, please let somebody call me. Tony held his phone in his hand desperately waiting on his agent's number to pop up with good news.

It was the eighth and final round. This was it.

"I'll be back, Momma," Tony said as he walked upstairs and went in the bathroom. He closed the door, leaned over on the sink, and prayed.

Please, God. Don't do this to me. I worked all my life for this moment. Just give me a chance, God. Please just give me a chance. One shot is all I

*need, God. Please let me get picked up by a team. I
need to get my family out of here. Please, God,
answer just this one prayer. Amen. I love you, God.*

Tony got up off of the sink and returned to the
living room with Momma and his brothers and saw
that the draft had ended. Tony closed his eyes and
dropped his head. The most humiliating,
embarrassing feeling circulated through his inner
body. His iPhone laid on his lap, he felt like
everybody was staring at him.

Then Tony's phone went off.

"Hello," he answered, putting his phone on
speaker.

It was his agent, Larry, on the phone.

"Hey, Tony. We have five teams interested in
you."

"Ahhhhhhh!" Max, Frank, Momma, and
everybody jumped up screaming.

He jumped up. "Shhhh! Shhhh!" Tony said,
smiling and putting his index finger to his lips,
trying to get them to quiet down.

Momma was hugging on Tony tight as tears of
joy poured down her face.

"Cincinnati has a great offer on the table with a
six-figure guaranteed signing bonus. I think that's
the best route," Larry told Tony.

"Let's do it," Tony said.

His heart smiled as he hung up with Larry. He
looked up and pointed to the ceiling as Momma

squeezed his abs, leaving his shirt soaking wet from her tears.

Thank you, God, for answering my prayer. Thank you, Man, you never let me down.

Chapter Twenty-Two

"Zeee 1079 this is yo' boy DJ Ty. It's a big night tonight for the city. Big Monday hosted by Frank each and every Monday. Big shout out to my boy, Tony for getting picked up by Cincinnati. We doin' it real big tonight at the Sunnyspot. Ladies free all night come on out and show my boy some love for putting East Cleveland on the map! Tony congratulations boyyyyy."

When they pulled up to the club Tony was surprised to see how many people showed up.

"Damnnnn, this shit crazy," Stew said. The line was wrapped around the building. There were two owners of the bar; one of them played the cut and never really showed his face. The other one stayed in the back room watching cameras monitoring the club. One of the owners of the bar sent two security guards outside to let Tony and his brothers in through the side door. The owner came out in a white T-shirt.

"Hey, what's up, my man?" Congratulations!" The owner greeted Tony, welcoming him home.

"Thanks!" Tony replied

"Hey, you two!" The owner said to the security guards.

"What's up, boss man?" they responded.

"Stay with them all night. Don't let them out your sight. This is family right here!" He said as he patted Tony's shoulder as they entered the club.

The club was so packed, they couldn't move. The cameraman snapped consecutive shots of Tony and his brothers, flashing the lights while the DJ announced his arrival as they followed the owner through the crowd to their section.

"Tony is in the building!" the DJ screamed into the microphone. Tony sat down on the couch while everybody around him turned up to Meek Mill's "Dreams and Nightmares. All Tony's brothers stood on the couch rapping the lyrics.

"Then I bought that new Ferrari, hater rest in peace.

Hater rest in peace, rest in peace to the parking lot.

Phantom so big, can't even fit in the parking spot.

You ain't talkin' bout my niggas then what you talkin' bout?

Gangstas move in silence, nigga and I don't talk a lot.

I don't say a word. I don't say a word.

Was on my grind and now I got what I deserve, fuck nigga!"

The club turned into a concert when the beat broke down, people in the crowd was shoulder to shoulder drenched in sweat as everybody continued rapping the lyrics.

"Hold up wait a minute, y'all thought I was finished? When I bought that Aston Martin y'all thought it was rented."

Tony stood up on the couch and smiled at the atmosphere when a thick dark-skinned girl approached him.

"Hey, Tony," she said smiling ear to ear.

He leaned over so he could hear her as they screamed over the music.

"What's up, Tamika?" Tony replied. Tamika was a girl Tony went to high school with but hadn't seen since the graduation. Tamika had been eyeing Tony since he walked in through the side door.

"Congratulations, Tony! I'm so proud of you," she yelled over the music looking up at him, flirting, smiling.

"Thanks," Tony replied nonchalantly.

"You should call me when you leave here." She flirted as she licked her lips slowly, stretching her bubble gum out of her mouth.

Tony grew a smirk on his face. "I'm good, love. Enjoy," he said as he turned his back towards her and went back into the section with his brothers. She stood in that spot, stuck.

The club was so hot, everybody was drenched in sweat rapping the lyrics to YFN Lucci's, *Young Fly*

Nigga and the atmosphere was lovely. As hot as it was, it was all smiles, and everyone was having a good time. The bottle girl tapped Frank on his leg as he stood on the couch.

"What's up?" Frank screamed over the music looking at the bottle girl

"You good?" She asked, giving the thumbs up signal.

"Naw, get me a bottle of D'ussé and get Tony a Voss water," Frank said.

Tony looked at Frank as if he was having déjà vu.

"Ahhhh what's up with my nigga?" DJ approached Tony with a big smile with his hand extended.

DJ was a short fly brown-skinned dude with dreads. He occasionally wore designer glasses, and he was wearing some tonight with a white Adidas tracksuit with his dreads in a bun.

"I ain't seen you in a minute, bra. How you been?" Tony asked. After Tony spoke to DJ, he didn't like the vibe he got after their exchange. Tony tapped Frank on his shoulder.

"What's up, bra?" Frank asked.

"I'm ready to go. I'm gettin' tired," Tony replied

"We just got here, bra. Chill!" Frank said brushing Tony off.

Tony sat back down on the couch and took a sip of his Voss water. "What up, bra? You good?" Stew asked, checking on Tony.

"I'm ready to go, bra," Tony said. "I gotta jump on the road early tomorrow to sign my contract."

"Ok, we out then," Stew said as he tapped Frank on his leg. Frank stood up in front of the section on the couch vibing to the music.

"Come on, y'all. We out," Stew said, leading his brother, Tony, out of the club.

"Hold up, bra! One more song!" Frank said calling after Stew.

"Naw, nigga we out." Stew walked back and yanked Frank off the couch. They wiggled through the crowded club and exited out the main entrance. Girls and guys stared as they left the building.

"Come on, bro! Hurry up, they goin' to the parking lot!" the one dude said to the other.

The whole night, Tony and his brothers were being stalked by a group of guys from the projects. Frank, Stew, Tony, Mell and Chris left out with the security guards escorting them through the parking lot headed to their car to go home. Suddenly, six guys with hoodies came from behind and bum rushed through Tony and his brothers, cutting off their path to the car and causing a confrontation. They stood toe to toe in the middle of the parking lot.

"Man, what the fuck wrong with y'all niggas?" Stew said, stepping in front of his brothers. Five of the six guys drew guns from underneath their hoodies.

"What you wanna do, bitch ass nigga?" The guys said as they cocked their guns. The two security guards froze up and stepped to the side once they saw the guns drawn, leaving Stew and his little brothers face to face with the six guys.

Tony went into shock. His heart dropped, and he stepped to the back behind his brothers.

The club let out and hundreds of people were outside mingling. There was commotion going on all over the parking lot. A group of women were arguing about a cellphone on the other side of the lot. It was beginning to get chaotic. Then Frank stepped up in front of his brothers to defuse the confrontation.

"Come on, y'all. We just came out here to have a good time. We don't want no problems. My little brother came out here. He just got drafted and we just came out to celebrate," he said, pointing at Tony as he stood in the back.

As Frank went on, Tony hoped and prayed the guys would retreat so they could get to their car and leave.

"Y'all been drinking, we been drinking. It ain't worth it to be pullin' out guns and fightin' each other like this." Frank continued speaking and more guys started walking up behind the guys from the Projects. Their entourage grew quickly as they stood toe to toe in the fairly lit parking lot.

"Yeah man, he right," one of the guys responded. "Put up the guns. Let's go this shit ain't worth it."

The guy who said that was probably their leader because the guys put away their guns quickly.

Frank turned around to his brother and said, "Come on, y'all. We out."

Tony breathed a sigh of relief.

Suddenly one of the dudes said, "Man, fuck that." He ran up and punched Frank in the jaw from the blind side.

Frank hit the ground. Gunshots rang continuously over his head as everybody ran through the parking lot screaming. He stayed down using the car as a shield. Tony ducked down and ran back towards the club tripping and falling trying to get out the way of the gunfire. He feared for his life as he heard bullets fly passed his head.

The bullets ricocheted off the brick walls of the club as Tony raced to hide. He finally made it in the front of the building away from the gunfire. Tony turned and saw his brother, Frank, about 500 feet away on his hands and knees in the middle of the crossfire. It looked like a scene in the Wild Wild West.

Frank and Tony made eye contact and Frank noticed Tony get into a running position like he was about to come towards him.

"Noooooo!" Frank yelled at Tony, waving him away with tears in his eyes. Tony had a look on his face Frank had never seen before.

"Stay over there!" Frank yelled as he put his hands together in a praying position pleading with

Tony not to run over towards him. As bad as it hurt Tony not to go grab his brother, he stayed back fighting tears and squeezing his fist. Frank stayed crouched down behind the car as Tony was forced to watch Frank defenseless in a war.

"Stay down!" Stew yelled at Frank, kneeling nearby. The gunshots stopped, and the parking lot became close to silent after at least three minutes of nonstop shooting.

Then Frank heard a *click, click, click.* "They're out of bullets," Frank whispered to himself. He jumped up and ran out the parking lot but then he heard more shots.

"Ahhhhhh!" Frank screamed after a bullet pierced his ankle. His leg went numb and he stumbled to the ground.

"Nooooo!" Tony cried when he saw Frank drop down and try to hobble out of the way.

"SHIT!" Stew came running through the parking lot when he saw his brother hurt. He ran recklessly into the crossfire shooting. He snatched Frank up by his shirt collar and turned back around; ducking, running, and shooting behind him as he pulled Frank out of the parking lot trying to slow down their gunfire. Bullets were hitting cars and shattering windshields.

"Get in the car, Tony!" Stew yelled.

Tony was lost, scared, and confused looking at Stew run towards him carrying Frank. He jumped into the passenger seat Stew jumped into the driver seat and sped away quickly.

"You alright, bra?" Stew asked Frank.

"Yeah, I'm good," Frank replied.

Tony sat in the car in complete shock. His heart was pounding as they drove up the street on two flat tires and a shot-out windshield looking for the nearest place to park the car. The closest place around was their Uncle Bunky's house two streets over from where they were.

Stew pulled out his phone and called Momma. As he pulled into Uncle Bunky's driveway, Tony and Frank punched in the key code and ran inside Uncle Bunky's house while he was sleeping.

Frank grabbed some peroxide and an Ace bandage and sat on the living room couch to wrap his ankle. As Frank wrapped his ankle, he looked up at Tony and saw him on his knees with his hands locked together praying.

It was 2:39 a.m. when Stew called Momma. She was sleeping with her phone next to her ear. Whenever her phone rang that late, she immediately jumped up out her sleep, hoping her boys was okay.

"Hello?" she said talking in her sleep.

"Momma, can you come get us from Uncle Bunky house? The car got shot up and..." Before Stew could finish his sentence, Momma jumped out the bed screaming and crying.

"Where is my baby? Where is my baby?" She screamed as she tied her robe and slipped into her house shoes.

"He's right here, Momma. Chill," Stew said as he shut off the engine and stepped out the car, standing in Uncle Bunky's driveway holding the phone to his ear.

"Boy, what the hell you mean chill? If y'all let something happen to my baby..."

"Oh shit!" Stew said as he hung the phone up and ducked down behind his car as a police cruiser came driving slowly up Uncle Bunky's street. He ducked down slowly tip toeing aside the car as the cruiser passed.

He crept into the back yard, tossed the gun in the trashcan on the side of the house and went inside through the back door.

"You alright, bra?" Stew asked Tony, looking at him with his head down.

Tony didn't respond. He just sat on the edge of the couch with his elbows on his knees and his hands locked together, shaking his head.

The room was completely silent. Stew walked over and sat down on the couch in between Frank and Tony and put his arm around Tony's shoulder.

"Pick yo' head up, bra. Be happy that we all still alive. Those niggas tried to kill us! Dat would've ruined everything for..."

"Man, I just wanna leave, bra," Tony interrupted. "I just wanna leave."

Frank sat next to Stew wrapping his leg and beating himself up mentally.

Momma and Chris pulled in Uncle Bunky's driveway at the same time. While Uncle Bunky was downstairs sleeping, Momma walked into the house.

"I can't take this shit no more. Come on, baby" Momma pulled Tony off the couch by his wrist, stormed back out the door, and headed home.

Frank, Stew, and Chris sat in the living room ten minutes before they left out and went to Chris's apartment. Momma and Tony were cruising up the road on their way to Momma's.

"We goin' to get your bags and I'm takin you to Cincinnati. You don't need to be up here around this shit," Momma said.

Tony took a deep breath. "Thank you," he said as he reclined his seat staring at the night sky thru the sunroof as they drove to Momma's house.

Chapter Twenty-Three

"What the hell?" Momma said as she looked up in her rear-view mirror. Tony sat up in the passenger seat and saw Cleveland Heights police cruisers swarming him and Momma.

"Driver, pull over and step out with your hands in the air!" The car was surrounded. Momma slowly pulled over to the curb right near the Marathon gas station.

The Marathon gas station was the place everybody went to hang out after the clubs closed. A lot of people were outside when the police surrounded Momma and Tony. As the crowd formed and watched. Tony's heart dropped. He never saw anything like this. It looked like the scene in *Set It Off* when Queen Latifah was in a standoff.

"What the hell is this about?" Momma asked as she stepped out with her hands in the air. The officers pointed their weapons at Momma as they walked towards her screaming.

"Turn around and keep your hands where I can see them!" Momma turned and faced the hood of her white four door Nissan Altima, squinting her eyes with a confused look on her face. Everybody at Marathon stared as the police put Momma into handcuffs.

"Passenger, step out the car with your hands up!" Tony stepped out the car with his hands in the air. The second he stepped out the car, deep sighs were heard from the onlookers.

Someone shouted, "No, y'all got the wrong person! He just got drafted to the NFL!"

When Tony heard the girl scream, he turned to look, and the officer choked the back of his neck and pushed him on the car.

"He's not playing for anybody! He's goin' to jail for aggravated murder," the officer said.

Everything in Tony's body went numb. They pushed him into the backseat of the police car and took him to jail.

Just hours ago, he was at his all-time happiest and in a blink of an eye his entire life became a tragedy.

Momma was behind the cruiser where Tony was being held. They rode back to back on their way to Cleveland Heights police station while the crowd at the gas station watched.

Stew, Frank and Chris pulled to Chris' apartment. Chris had an apartment in downtown

Cleveland nobody knew about that was his secret space. The whole ride to Chris' apartment, Frank was in a daze. He stared out the window looking at Lake Erie as they drove 60mph on the freeway. What he saw in the parking lot was stuck in his head permanently. He just couldn't seem to get the images out of his head. That sight would haunt him for the rest of his life.

Momma and Tony arrived at the station. They looked at each other in handcuffs and Momma broke down screaming and fell to her knees.

"Ma'am..." the officers said as they tried to escort her into the police station.

Momma tried to pull herself together but couldn't. Seeing her baby in handcuffs was something she could never imagine. Tears uncontrollably poured down Tony's face as he walked into the station with the officer's hand in the back of his neck. They took Tony inside of a room with a table and one chair with a swinging light hanging from the ceiling.

"You have the right to remain silent. Anything you say can and will be used against you in a court of law."

As they read Tony his rights, the feeling that was going through his body was intangible. He tried to speak, but the words wouldn't leave his mouth.

"Go ahead tell us what happened," the detectives said as he leaned over on the table, looking at Tony staring at the floor.

Tony's eyes didn't move and his mind went completely blank.

Momma was in the next room directly across from Tony screaming, crying. "Get my baby outta here! He didn't do nothing! Get my baby outta here!" Momma yelled as she cried, drooling on the detective's floor.

"Here you go ma'am." The detective handed Momma a Kleenex.

"Calm down please, ma'am," the detective said. "Just tell me what you know, and I'll do my best to help you. If Tony didn't have anything to do with this, we will find out and no charges will be filed against him. He will be out of here in time to sign his contract so tell us what you know."

"I know my baby ain't have nothin' to do with that. Stew was out there fighting them boys. It wasn't my baby." She took a deep breath. "My baby ain't have nothin' to do with that!" Momma screamed.

The detectives opened their notepads and started taking notes as Momma unconsciously went on a rant saying anything to get her baby Tony out of jail.

Max, Frank, Stew were downtown at Chris' apartment when Stew's phone rang.

"Hello?" Stew answered and stood up from the table as he pulled his phone away from his face and looked at it. Momma was screaming through the phone.

"Momma, I can't hear you. Stop screaming!" Stew said.

Max, Frank and Chris stared at Stew to see what was happening.

"You in jail?" Stew asked.

"Yes! You need to bring your ass down here! You got my baby's name in a fuckin homicide!"

Stew dropped the phone. The apartment was silent.

"Homicide?" he thought to himself as he dropped his head.

"My life is over," Stew said softly as he fell back on the living room couch. The detectives made a verbal agreement for Stew and Frank to turn themselves in for questioning in and return they would cut Tony and Momma loose with no charges.

Stew and Frank made their way to the Police Department. Tony only had eight hours left to be in Cincinnati to sign his contract, and it was 4-hour drive from Cleveland. Frank and Stew knew they had to hurry to get there before anybody found out Tony's name was involved.

Frank and Stew arrived at the station. As they were walking in, DJ was walking out. He gave them a head nod and walked into the parking lot as they passed.

They walked up to the front window and told the receptionist who they were, and in seconds, police officers swarmed around them and took them into custody. Four officers stood behind Frank and Stew on the elevator on their way to get booked.

"Well if it isn't the two dumb asses who ruined their baby brother's entire career."

"What you mean? Y'all bout let him go, right? That was the deal," Frank asked.

"That's what you thought?" The officers laughed.

"Shut up, Frank. Don't talk to these pigs." Stew said.

"You're never gonna see daylight again after what your mom told us about you." The white officer said, laughing and high-fiving the black detective. They walked out of the elevator towards the booking desk looking in each cell they passed looking for Tony

"Frank? Stew?" They heard Tony's scream from down the hall. Stew and Frank looked around to see him, but they only heard his voice.

Stew yelled "Yeah, bra! We here now and they're 'bout to let you go!"

Tony didn't shout back, he got silent. "You hear me bra?" Stew yelled out loud.

Tony replied, "No, they ain't. They just charged me."

"What? Charged you with what?" Stew turned around and looked at the cops. "Man, what the fuck y'all charge him for? He ain't do shit!" Stew screamed as the officers laughed in his face. They threw him into the cell and slammed the door.

Momma got released with no charges. Tony, Stew, and Frank sat in the cold jail cells.

"Aye Tony?" Stew yelled with his face threw the gap of the bars screaming across the hall.

"Yeah?" Tony replied

"God got us, bra. Don't worry."

"Ha haaa! We'll see how much God can do about this one, dumb ass," the officer said, walking away from the cells.

It was only hours before Tony needed to bond out and be in Cincinnati.

The minute Momma was released, she scrambled around the city scraping up whatever she could from family members, coaches and friends. Some came through and some slammed the door in her face after hearing what happened. In the end, Momma posted bond for Tony.

"Come on, baby. We gotta hit the road," Momma said as her and Tony ran down the hall out the front door of the police station. Outside, the media had the parking lot full.

A blonde, female news reporter asked, "What made you hide evidence from a homicide, do you know how important that is?" She walked on the side of him pushing the mic towards his mouth.

Tony and Momma power walked to the car as the reporters continued to hound and harassed him with questions. They jumped in the car and hit the highway. After a long four-hour ride, Tony and Momma arrived in Cincinnati. Momma pulled into the parking lot of the facility parked and walked up the long row of stairs. It felt like the gateway to heaven as Tony wrapped his arm around Momma's shoulder.

They entered the huge building. The whole front entryway was made of glass. The floor, walls, and ceiling were made of shiny white marble. Tony was lost for words as he looked around at players in their NFL uniforms practicing and stretching on the indoor field and working out with the training equipment. He dedicated his entire life to this and it was a dream come true.

"Hi, may I help you?" the receptionist asked as Tony and Momma approached the front desk. Tony gave the receptionist his name, and she directed him to the scouting course on the third floor.

"Good afternoon," Cincinnati's scouting director said as he gave Tony a firm handshake with a huge smile. Tony stomach was turning in every which way possible, praying they didn't receive that false news about him that happened in Cleveland.

"Good afternoon," Tony replied, looking the man in his eyes.

"Well, Tony..." he said as he walked sat down at his desk and locked his hands. "Unfortunately, we have to put your contract on hold due to allegations

of you being involved in a homicide in another city."
Tony dropped his head.

"He didn't have anything to do with that! His
brothers are in jail for that," Momma whined.

"I understand, but he has to clear that up with
the courts before we can go any further."

"After I get my name cleared from all of this, can
I come play? I promise I'ma be the best defensive
player y'all ever saw. Just sign me and see," Tony
pleaded.

"Yes, as long as you get this cleared before
training camp and practice begins. I will have this
contract right here with your name on it ready for
you to sign," he said as he patted the manila folder
with Tony's name and position on it. Momma was
quietly crying as the two sat in front of her talking.

"Thank you so much."

Momma sobbed. "Thank you," she said.

Tony shook his hand. "Thank you. I will be back
before training ends," Tony said with strong eye
contact, hugging Momma with one arm. Momma
had Tony's stomach soaked with her tears. Tony
and Momma walked out the facility together.

"Thank you, Jesus," they said in unison.

Chapter Twenty-Four

The drive back to Cleveland felt much shorter than it felt going to Cincinnati. As they got off the freeway headed to Momma's house, Tony still couldn't believe what his life had become in a blink of an eye. He was so deep in thought; so many things went through his mind. He couldn't stop blaming himself.

"This all my fault I should've never came home. I should have listened to Coach Randolph."

"Oh, my God!" Momma burst out screaming as she turned down her street and saw her house in flames. The fire department had the whole street blocked completely. Police cruisers were out, along with the whole neighborhood.

"Nooooo!" Momma screamed as she parked the car, jumped out, and ran up the street towards her house.

"Ma'am, you can't go down there!" An officer said, blocking her path.

"That's my house!" Momma yelled, slapping down his hand.

"Momma, come on and just step back!" Tony said, pulling her back from the hoe ass officer. The chief firefighter and the head detectives all approached Momma.

"Ma'am, can we have a word with you?"

"Yes. What happened? There's nobody in my house, and I know I didn't leave anything on the stove," Momma said panicking.

"Yes, we know. That's why we're here to talk," the detective said as he pulled out a notepad and pen. "This fire wasn't accidental, someone set this intentionally. Do you have any enemies or someone you know that may have done this?"

"No. Nobody would have never done this but my ex-husband and he's in jail."

Tony watched the firemen on the ladder extended from the truck as they sprayed while Momma's house burned.

"God, what is going on?" Momma cried.

This was all a big nightmare for Tony, Momma, and the family. So many thoughts were going through Tony's mind.

A voice came upon him. "God gives his toughest battles to his strongest warriors. Take it personal."

He took a deep breath and stood there squinting like the sun was in his eyes. After a few hours, the fire department managed to extinguish the fire.

"I can't believe this!" Momma said. Tony had given Momma his signed senior jersey from Arizona State University, which was framed and hung up in the center of the living room. It was the first thing people saw when they entered the house. Momma and Tony walked up to the house and saw his framed jersey burnt to a crisp. Tony slapped his forehead and gripped his face as he slid his hand down in disbelief.

"Huhhhhh," he exhaled in frustration. Tony, Momma, and Max moved in with Chris in his apartment downtown until they got things situated with getting a new house for Momma.

Chris was brown skinned with a baby face and brush waves. He didn't really talk much but was an extremely helpful and modest person. He would give anyone the shirt off his back without thinking twice about it.

He, Frank and Tony had a strong bond that grew over the years after taking so many trips to Arizona for Tony's games and so many more incidents behind closed doors. Unforeseen forces bounded them so close, it was crazy.

Frank was released on bond after being charged with obstruction of justice for not cooperating with authorities. Stew was charged with aggravated murder and sent to county jail.

After Momma unconsciously went on a rant, she put Stew in a terrible position. She told detectives Stew was her only child who carried a gun.

The truth was that Stew carried a gun on him at all time just for life or death situations. Stew was the only brother who really knew the streets and what it came with. He knew what type of hating people were in the streets and he always had to be prepared or he would get buried.

Nothing could have happened to make Momma feel any worse than she had, especially after the phone call from Stew. He cursed her out so badly and called her a snitch.

"How could you tell on your own son? Your own child? You gave birth to me!" Stew shouted through the phone.

Momma couldn't do anything about it. She'd been under pressure, in jail and all she could think of at time was getting Tony out of jail. She would've told them anything to do that.

But, it was too late to take back her words now. She was under a type of pressure she never imagined. Momma cried every morning in the bathroom mirror and told herself keep fighting and praying. She did the same routine daily. Tony watched Momma break down day after day.

The news spread through the city and across the world so fast every high school, beauty salon, and barbershop made it the topic of their conversations. The family was embarrassed to be seen in public. Tony was forced to watch Momma cry herself to sleep in Chris' apartment every night, and it tore him apart mentally knowing he couldn't do anything but wait until they cleared his name from this.

Court was a month away and the contract deadline was two days after that. Momma sat on the couch chain-smoking cigarettes.

"Aye, Momma?" Tony called her name as he sat on the living room couch across from her.

"Yes, baby?" Momma replied.

He paused for about 10 seconds and sat up before he spoke. "I love you and we're gonna be good alright."

"I love you too, baby." She paused as she stared into Tony's eyes and repeated, "I love you too." A tear rolled down her cheek as Momma pulled the cover over her shoulder and fell asleep.

Frank and Chris were pulling off from the Taco Bell drive thru about two in the morning.

"Take me to my whip bra," Frank said as he stuffed his mouth with a Cheesy Gordita Crunch. Frank kept his car parked in his baby mama's driveway.

"You 'bouta take it in for the night?" Chris asked looking back and forth at from his rear-view mirror and Frank.

"Naw, not yet. I'm 'bouta go chill with this girl," he said. Frank and Chris drove down Euclid choppin' it. Chris continued looking up at his rearview mirror as he drove.

"Somethin' don't feel right," Chris said as he pulled up to Frank's car.

"What you talkin' about?" Frank asked.

"I don't know, bra. Just be careful," Chris said as he dapped up Frank. Chris started popping Ecstasy pills. The pills made him seem paranoid and Frank hated that about him.

"Yup. You too, bra. Call me when you get to the house," Frank said as he ran up the front porch, unlocked the door and walked into the living room. The house was dark. The TV mounted on the wall barely lit the room.

"DAD!" Naz screamed as he jumped off the living room couch into Frank's arms.

"W'sup boy? what you doin' up so late?"

"Me... an.. and my umm, Mommy watchin' TV."

Frank walked over to the couch with Naz in one arm leaned over and saw his baby mama asleep.

"Stop fakin'!" He said, slapping her on her butt while she laid on her stomach across the couch.

"Boy, stooooppp!" She whined.

Frank's phone rang. "W'sup, bra?" he answered when he saw Chris calling.

"Man, it's some niggas ridin' around in a black truck looking fishy. Be careful."

Frank smacked his teeth. "Alright, bra. Good lookin.'" He said shaking his head as he hung up the phone.

Frank kissed his son and laid him on top of his mother. "I'll be back," Frank said as he left.

"Where you goin'?" she asked.

"I'ma be back, man. Damn," he said with an attitude as he slammed the door. He jumped in his car and left.

Naz was watching TV for an hour after Frank left the house.

"Dad?" He said as he noticed a man walking through the dining room.

Naz squinted to try to see through the darkness but the light from the TV screen blurred his vision. He wiped his eyes to get a clearer view. When he removed his hands, a masked man stood in his face, holding a gun. "Where yo' daddy at, lil' nigga?" he said, forcing his pistol against Naz's head.

"Owwww!" He whined, rubbing his forehead. His mother rolled over in her sleep and opened one eye when she heard the man's voice.

"Ahhhh!" she screamed loud.

"Shut the fuck up, bitch! If you scream again, I'm killing this lil' nigga," he said as he tightened the muscles in his lips.

She tried her best to keep quiet as he tied their hands and feet with plastic zip ties.

"I want my daddy!" Naz cried

"I want him too, lil' nigga! Now shut the fuck up!"

He talked to Frank's baby mama as he tied her feet together.

"He killed my brother at the club the other day. My mama ain't stopped cryin'. I'm bouta kill that nigga so his momma can feel how our momma feeling right now."

Two more masked men came running from upstairs.

"He ain't up there."

"Where the nigga at?" he said, snatching her phone off the arm of the couch.

"I don't know!" she cried.

"Well, call the nigga and you better not give no hints to him over the phone or I'm killin this lil' nigga!" He tossed the phone on her lap. She couldn't stop crying and shaking.

Frank was laid up with the girl he met from Instagram when he saw his baby mama calling and pressed Ignore. She called again and again, letting the phone ring on speakerphone. The three masked men stood over her with their guns.

"Man, why da fuck she calling like this?" he said as he silenced his phone.

"Gimme dis, muthafucka." The masked man snatched the phone from Frank's baby mama and sent a text to Frank's phone."

Frank rolled over grabbed his phone and read the message: "Come home."

He jumped up and left.

Tony and Momma were knocked out on the couch across from each from other. When

Momma's phone rang, she woke up scared. She answered and got the devastating news. She screamed and her reaction woke Tony.

"What's wrong, Momma?" Tony said as he snatched the cover off of himself and jumped off the couch.

"We gotta go, we gotta go!" Momma cried, slipping into some flip-flops and running out the door. Tony was half-asleep and didn't know what was happening, but he knew it had to be serious the way Momma reacted. He slipped on some flip-flops and ran out behind Momma in basketball shorts and a tank top.

Momma pulled up to the scene. There were five police cruisers and an ambulance in front of the house.

"Momma what happened over here?" Tony asked.

The scene was like a horror movie. Cops and ambulances everywhere. Momma didn't respond, she just cried as she and Tony got out the car.

"Where's my baby?" Momma cried after she heard Frank, Naz, and Naz's mother were kidnapped.

"Hey, get back!" A Black cop with curly hair stepped up with his arm out and yelled at Momma as she tried to walk on the porch.

"No, she's good," the Lieutenant ordered, slapping the officer's hand off Mommas chest.

The curly haired cop gave the Lieutenant a nasty look. Tony followed behind Momma looking for Frank.

"Where my brother at?" he asked in a concerned voice. The entire neighborhood was outside standing on their porches, watching the police surround the house to investigate the incident.

"Uncle Tony!" Naz broke free from his mom's arms and screamed. He ran and jumped into his uncle's arms. Tony picked him up and hugged him. "Uncle Tony, I wish I had my "Call of Duty" guns when the bad guys was in there," Naz said.

Tony hugged his nephew, pushing the back of his head onto his big shoulders and squeezing him. Tony fought back tears while holding his nephew in his arms.

"What happened, bra?" Tony asked as he walked up on Frank.

"My baby momma texted me and said come home. When I got here, I opened the door to dudes with pistols in my face."

As Frank went on, Tony stared into Frank's eyes and listened thoroughly while tears rolled down his face. Anger was building up inside of him. Max had gotten the news. He pulled up, jumped out the car and went to the group of officers standing in a huddle in front of the house.

"Y'all gonna find out who did this shit or y'all gonna just stand around like everything is cool?"

He asked, holding out his arms.

"Calm down! Our detectives and investigators are on the job, sir."

"Y'all still ain't found out nothin' about my Momma's house being burnt down, my little brother being shot. Now my nephew got kidnapped and all y'all got to say is calm down"

"We're trying to solve the matter." The short white officer went back and forth with Max.

"Y'all not tryna do shit but put my babies in jail and ruin their lives!" Momma butted in.

"Your babies ruined their own goddamn lives!" the curly head black cop said.

"Nigga, why you talkin' to my Momma like that?" Max said, snatching off his shirt.

"Hey, watch it." The officer stepped back and put his hand on his pistol, giving Max a look like he will blow out his brains if he made a move.

Later that day, Max, Chris, Tony and Momma sat on the porch while Naz and Frank played catch in the front yard. Quana pulled up with Pierre in the car.

"Ahhhhhhhh!" Max yelled in excitement.

They hadn't seen their nephew in five years. Pierre was dark-skinned and slim He stood about 5"11 and had a six-pack and a full beard.

"What's up, Unc?" Pierre said. Everybody hugged Pierre and showed him unconditional love.

Tony sat on the porch stairs talking to Pierre and Max.

"I just feel like my life is falling apart, man," Tony said.

"Look, Unc. You got two options: stand up or lay down. What you gon' do?" Pierre asked.

Five years in jail had turned Pierre into a hardnosed bull. Whatever problems came to him, there was only one thing to do: deal with them. That's what he came home preaching. "I ain't gone lie I thought I was gon' come home and be able to watch you play in the league soon as I get out but now I gotta wait to this clear but that don't..."

POW! POW! POW!

Pierre stopped mid-sentence after hearing three gunshots go off on the next street. Hearing gunshots in that neighborhood was like hearing birds chirping at six a.m.—absolutely normal.

"What the...?"

Tony got up from the porch stairs and ran into the house. The shots sounded too close for him. Pierre, Max and Frank sat there. The gunshots didn't frighten them one bit.

Tony ran upstairs dropped to his knees. With his elbows on the edge of the bed, he prayed.

"Dear Lord, please take this cloud from over my family and me. Please. I don't know what I did, but I'm sorry. Just please help us get out of this dark place, God. Please.

Chapter Twenty-Five

Tony and Frank sat side-by-side dressed up in all black like they were going to a wedding. They waited in the crowded lobby on the 18th floor in the justice center for both of their attorneys to come and give them some news. Momma, Max, Quana, and the rest of the family sat behind them. The lobby was so packed with support, there wasn't even enough room for everyone to sit. Tony stared at the courtroom door with his hands locked together, anxiously tapping his Hugo Boss dress shoes on the floor. He was waiting for his attorney to bring him some good news. Frank and Tony had the same look in their eyes as they stared at the door. Frank looked over at Tony and tapped his leg.

"Bra" Frank said with a slight pause as they made eye contact "We gon be cool. God got us. Alright?" Frank whispered.

"I know. I just don't want y'all to go to jail I don't know what I'ma do without my brothers."

"We not goin' to jail, bra. They're gonna dismiss this. God knows the real. He's not gonna let this happen to us." Frank and Tony went back and forth in the lobby.

Stew was being escorted through the back hallways of the jail. Shackled from his wrist to his ankles, his long dreads fell over his face as he took each step. Dressed in the orange county jail jumpsuit, he headed to the courtroom. He knew he had to make something happen today because Tony's contract was going to get snatched off the table if this matter didn't get solved today. This was it!

It was the final court date after a bunch of continuances. It was Tony's last chance.

Stew sat down on the bench in the holding cell behind the courtroom as his attorney approached the cell with a stack of manila folders. His attorney was an older black man with a shiny baldhead, a goatee, and a very professional accent.

"How are you this morning, Stew? Hanging in there?"

"I'm good. What's up with my little brothers though?" Stew asked through the window of the holding cell.

"Well I haven't spoken with their attorneys quite yet," he said as he scanned through his folders.

"Aye, man. Let's just get this over with today. I'm tired of sitting in this county."

"That's the plan. The prosecutor came to an agreement on a ten-year sentence for you. I know it's a lot of time, but it's better than a possible maximum sentence of twenty-two years."

"I will take the ten, man. Just get my little brother out of this... whatever you do."

Stew and his attorney went back and forth while Tony and Frank anxiously waited on their attorneys to come through the door. Tony looked back at Momma sitting between Max, Chris, Quana, and the pastor of her church. Momma was crying, shaking her knee, and dabbing her eyes with Kleenex trying not to smear her makeup.

"Hold up, bra. I'll be right back." Frank jumped up when he saw his attorney come through the door. He walked quickly over to him. Frank's attorney was a tall white male with blonde hair and a sharp pointy nose.

"What's up? What they talkin' about?" Frank asked.

"Well, they put a deal on the table." He paused as he started looking through his folder. He pulled out a small package.

"They've agreed to dismiss all charges against Tony today."

"YES!" Frank said, he lifted his head and pumped his fist.

"But only if you and Stew agree to the charges against you."

Frank snatched the package out his lawyer's hand. "Ok, where do I sign?"

"Well, wait a minute. I know you want your brother to play football but are you sure this contract is guaranteed?"

"Man, whether it is or not, he don't have nothin' to do with this and it's ruining his life," Frank said.

"I understand. But this judge is tough and you can face up to three years for this."

"Man, just get Tony's name out of this."

"I'll be back. I'm gonna confirm everything and finalize the deal, but when we go in this courtroom and she asks you, 'Do you have anything to say,' I want you to say, 'No.'"

"Okay, bet." Frank turned around smiling. As he walked back, Tony jumped up in suspense.

"What happened, bra?" Tony asked as he stood toe to toe with Frank. He looked up at Tony and smiled.

"They're about to drop all charges against you today," Frank said.

"What about you and Stew?" Tony asked.

"We had to cop out, but they dropped Stew's murder to a manslaughter."

"Naw, bra. You trippin. We ain't do nothin, go take that back! HEYYY!" Tony yelled trying to get the lawyer's attention, pushing Frank aside.

"Naw, bra. It's cool," Frank said, pulling Tony back.

"Man, you can't go to jail! What I'ma do without you and Stew?" Tony's eyes instantly became red and swollen as tears quickly filled his eyes. It was tearing him apart knowing he could possibly loose his brothers to the system.

"I just want you to play football and live your life, bra. Plus, they ain't bouta send me to jail for no obstruction. I'm probably bouta get some probation or something."

The bailiff walked into the lobby and called them into the courtroom. Tony and Frank walked side by side into the courtroom. Momma followed her boys with a huge crowd of people trailing behind her, trying to squeeze into the courtroom. When Tony and Frank entered the courtroom, they could not believe what they saw. Channel 5 and Fox News were set up inside the courtroom. The victim's family was seated to the left side of the courtroom along with DJ.

Frank looked at DJ sitting with the victim's family and shook his head. He and Tony approached the podium.

The bailiff went to the back to bring Stew into the courtroom. Momma, Max, Quana and Chris sat in the front row. It was packed—filled to capacity and forty to fifty people waited outside the courtroom.

"All rise for the Honorable Judge Maylene Safo!" the bailiff said.

Judge Safo was an older black woman with long pretty hair and glasses. She had a reputation of being tough to anyone who stood in front of her. She had been on the bench for so long she was sick of being lied to by criminal minded people. She had a habit of believing everyone who stood in front of her was trying to deceive and manipulate her in some way.

"You all may be seated," she said as she approached the bench.

The courtroom was so silent you could hear a pin drop. Her presence had everybody tense and nervous. The bailiff walked to the bench and whispered something in the judge's ear. She looked back at the bailiff and shook her head.

Tony and Frank's eyes were glued on Judge Safo, watching her every move. The bailiff walked to the back and escorted Stew into the courtroom. The second Stew stepped into the courtroom loud sighs were heard. He glanced at Momma and dropped his head.

Tears uncontrollably fell down Momma's face. Max looked at his three brothers standing side-by-side at the podium. Tony stood in the middle of his two older brothers with Stew to the right and Frank to the left.

"Good morning, your Honor," Tony's lawyer began to speak for him. "My client is an innocent college student who just came home for one night to celebrate with his family for..."

"Okay, I don't want to hear none of that. A parent lost her child here." The judge cut him off in the middle of his sentence.

The prosecutor stood. "May I speak, your Honor?" he said, raising his hand.

"Go ahead," she replied.

"We have agreed to drop all charges against Tony because he was proven to be innocent after his brother took full responsibility for his actions."

"Which one is Tony?" the judge asked.

Tony raised his hand. "Ok, we'll you're good to go." She said as she waved her hand.

The courtroom roared. Max, Quana and Chris hugged all over Momma. She jumped up and hugged Tony as he walked over and sat between them in the front row.

"Order in the court!" the judge yelled as she slammed her gavel. The courtroom instantly became as quiet as a library. Tony was happy, but not quite as excited as everybody else was. He was more concerned about his brothers.

"Good morning, your honor. My client is a very humble, quiet, down to earth businessman with a six-year-old son. This night he tried to defuse this situation to the best of his ability and I don't...

She cut Frank's attorney off. "Do you have anything to say?" she asked.

Frank had so much to say, but he kept it brief.

"I just want to apologize to the family for their loss," Frank said. The judge picked up a pen and start signing papers as she spoke.

"Well I'm sentencing you to do three years in the..."

"Nooooo!" Tony burst out crying. Stew dropped his head. Momma screamed.

The judge slammed her gavel. "Take him outta here!" she said. Two officers walked up behind Frank and slapped handcuffs tight on his wrist. As they escorted him out of the courtroom, he took one final look at his family.

Frank and Tony locked eyes, and Tony gave him the same look he had in the parking lot of the club, like he wanted to come run and grab him. Tony rocked back and forth with tears of pain rolling down his face.

Stew stood at the podium alone, ten toes down. Not knowing what to expect, he just watched his little brother get sentenced to three years in prison. He was beyond hurt.

"Excuse me, your honor? May I speak?" The victim's mom stood up and raised her hand.

"Go ahead," Judge Safo said.

"I think these are some nice young men, and I don't think they deserve to sit in prison for a long time. Yes, I lost my child and I am torn apart about it, but I also know what type of friends my child had. They were dangerous. He hung out with the wrong people. I would hate to see these young men's lives get shattered over this. As I'm looking around not one of my child's friends who was with him that night is present here in this courtroom. That's all I have to say." She sat back down and looked over at Momma.

Momma put her hands together in a praying position and softly said "Thank you."

The judge looked at Stew. "Do you have anything to say?"

"Yes, your Honor. First of all, I want to apologize to the family. I didn't mean to harm anybody that night I was just..."

"What do you mean you didn't mean to harm anyone? You were shooting out there like it was the Wild Wild West!" she said cutting Stew off.

"I saw my little brother Frank get shot, and I panicked. I was just trying to protect my family, your Honor. I'm not a killer by no means."

"Who is Frank?" she asked.

"The one you just gave three years."

"Oh. I didn't know he'd been shot. Where is your mom?" The judge asked.

Stew turned around and pointed at Momma. Judge Safo squinted at Momma as if she recognized her familiar face from somewhere then took her attention back to Stew, standing at the podium with his lawyer.

The whole time, Stew's attorney didn't say one word.

"Did you have an uncle name Reggie?" she asked, slowly removing her glasses from her face.

"Yes," Stew replied.

"He was a real big-time gangster and drug dealer?" she asked.

"Huh?" Stew replied with a confusing look. He turned around and looked back at Momma.

Momma had a confused look on her face as well.

"May I speak, your Honor?" Tony said as he stood with his hand in the air.

"Sure. What do you have to say?"

"My brothers mean everything to me, and my uncle did too. My family is not killers. We all got good hearts and we've been through a lot, your Honor. I don't know what I'm going to do without my brothers if you take them from us. My mother's been through so much. Just please try not to make it any worse than it is," Tony pleaded.

She gave Tony a blank stare, picked up her pen, and start writing and talking at the same time.

"I'm sentencing you to twenty-two years in the state penitentiary."

"Noooooooooooo!" Tony and Momma screamed at the top of their lungs as they fell to the floor.

"BITCH!" Max shouted as he stomped his foot. Stew's body went numb.

"What the fuck? Twenty-two years?" he said softly to himself.

"Man, what the fuck is goin' on?" He said to his attorney as they escorted him back into the holding cell. "I don't know," his lawyer replied, rubbing his baldhead. Stew took one last glance at his family as they broke down crying on the courtroom floor.

"I love you, bra," Max yelled at Stew over all the commotion as he tried to pull Tony and Momma off the floor. Frank heard the metal shackles on Stew's hands and feet coming back through the door from court.

"What happened, bra? What she give you?" Frank screamed from the holding cell.

"She maxed me out, bra," Stew said, hanging his head.

"Huh?" Frank replied.

"Twenty years, bra. Twenty-two years."

Frank was at a loss for words. It was literally hell on Earth. Everything that could've possibly gone wrong went wrong.

Tony marched out of the courthouse with a fierce look in his eye with Momma and the rest of his family trailing him. He had a serious look in his eye as if he was on a mission. Nothing or no one could stop him as he walked out of the Justice Center in downtown Cleveland.

"All charges dismissed. How do you feel?"

"Why did you come to Cleveland to party when you knew the crime rate is at an all-time high?"

The reporters rushed him with questions.

"Man, watch out!" Max said as he mugged the white cameramen to the ground. Everything that Tony had been through was more than enough to make him give up but giving up wasn't an option. It was personal.

The next day, Momma, Max, Chris and Tony piled up in her car and drove down the wet highway on their way to Cincinnati. Momma rocked side to side with both hands on the steering wheel, singing the lyrics to Sam Cooke's *A Change Is Gonna Come* cruising 65mph on the highway.

Nobody said a word to each other. Momma cried as she sang. This was her way of relieving stress and connecting with the Lord.

Tony's head was leaning against the passenger window. He stared out of it as the heavy rain splashed against the glass. He was deep in thought.

Chapter Twenty-Six

They arrived at the team facility for the second time.

"Wait right here, y'all. I'll be right back," Tony said as he jumped out the car and walked at a fast pace into the building and to the recruiter's office.

"ANTONIO!" The recruiting manager said with a big smile as he extended his hand. "How are you?

Tony took a deep breath and said "Blessed."

"That's great to hear, and I'm glad you got back with me in time for the training camp, follow me," he said as he grabbed a stack of folders from his desk and led Tony out his office and down the hallway. As Tony followed him down the hallway, he looked around at the white marble floor and 50 foot glass ceilings.

"This place is crazy," Tony said, following behind him.

"Yeah, they had to spend over $20 million rebuilding this place. You'll get used to it. This will be your new home."

Tony smiled. "Yeah. I could get used to this," he said, nodding his head.

"Give me one second, Antonio. I'm gonna let the GM know you're here," he told Tony as he walked into the GM's office.

"Alright," Tony said, staring out the glass window at downtown Cincinnati.

Tony knew he had to put everything that happened in the past few months behind him and get into tunnel vision. Football was the only way he knew how to get his mind off everything. No matter how much he went through with his family, when it was time to strap up and hit the field, everything was personal and anyone in front of him was going to feel how personal it was. He would feel sorry for a half back or wide receiver coming across the middle. With all the anger and hurt built inside of him, he's even more capable to hurt somebody next time he touches the field.

"TONY!"

"Yes sir?" Tony said, snapping out of a daze.

"Come on inside." He waved him in towards the GM's office.

"Pleasure to finally meet you." The GM stood up and shook Tony's hand.

"Thank you nice to meet you, too," Tony replied looking firmly into his eyes.

"Okay so here's the deal, unfortunately we have to take the contract off the table because of the severity of the case. With it being such a high-profile case, our organization could possibly lose ticket sales."

Tony's hands began to shake uncontrollably, he tried to speak but the words wouldn't come out.

"But... But..." Tony said.

"I'm sorry but good luck with your future," the GM said.

It took everything in Tony not to crumble. He lifted his head up, looked into the GM's eyes and thanked him as he stood up, walked out of the GM's office and left the facility. He got into the car and looked at Momma.

"What's the matter? Why do you look so sad?" Momma asked, looking over at Tony in the passenger seat. They sat inside the car in the parking lot of the facility.

"They took the contract off the table, Momma." Tony said as he dropped his head back on the headrest.

"Hell no! Contract off the table my ass!" Momma said as she opened the door and jumped out the car.

"No, Momma what is you doing?" Tony said as he grabbed Momma by her arm pulling her back into the car.

"Damn," Chris and Max said as they sat in the back seat, shaking their heads.

"It's alright, Momma. I'ma call my agent. It's more teams that will give me a shot," Tony said.

"Yeah, bra. Call him. He gotta make something shake," Chris said.

Momma rested her head on the steering wheel. "Jesus, Jesus, Jesus," she repeated.

"Come on, Momma. We out," Max said telling her to leave the parking lot.

Momma lifted her head off the steering wheel. Her face was soaking wet. She took a deep breath, wiped her tears with her hand, put on her seatbelt, and started driving. Tony felt his back was against the wall and his whole family was depending on him. This wasn't anything new being that he always felt that way, but the severity of it went up a million times more.

On the road back to Cleveland, Tony called his agent numerous times only to reach his voicemail. He was going into panic mode when suddenly his phone rang. He answered. It was Coach Randolph from Arizona State. He also had ties with teams in the NFL and CFL.

"What's goin' on, Tony? Any news?" he asked.

"Yeah," Tony replied in a dry tone. "Cincinnati took that contract off the table."

"That's alright. We still got more options. Let me make a few calls and hopefully I will call you back with some good news."

"Alright. Thanks, Coach," Tony said as he hung up his cell phone. He dropped his phone in his lap, leaned his head back against the headrest, and dozed off as Momma cruised on the highway back to home to Cleveland.

Two hours into the drive on their way back home from Cincinnati, Quana called Momma's phone panicking.

"Momma I don't know what's going on, but the police just kicked in my door! They have Pierre in the back of the police car!"

"Why are they taking him?" Momma yelled into the phone.

Tony jumped up out of his sleep. "The police taking who?" Tony asked.

Momma kept her ear to the phone trying to hear what was happening. Quana was on the other end of the phone yelling at the officers.

"Y'all stupid muthafuckas don't even have no search warrant! Y'all can't just come in here illegally searching my shit!" Quana yelled.

Quana talked extremely slow and when she yelled, she said one word at a time loud and slow. "Take the god damn handcuffs off my baby!" She continued cursing at the officers.

"Man, get the fuck off me!" Pierre yelled trying to break loose from the handcuffs.

"Stop resisting!" The officer yelled at Pierre right before he kicked the officer to the ground.

"Quana, what the hell is goin' on?" Momma yelled into the phone.

Tony, Max and Chris leaned in towards Momma's phone trying to hear what was happening. She put the phone on speakerphone.

"Momma, I don't know what's goin' on but they're saying something about a homicide last Tuesday on the next street over! Hold on, Momma."

"Get the hell off my baby!" Quana yelled in the background and hung up the phone.

Momma called Quana's phone back over and over but got no answer. She put the pedal to the medal on the highway to get back to Cleveland as fast as possible.

Tony sat in the passenger seat shaking his head, wondering to himself when will it stop. Tony looked at his phone and saw a message from Coach Randolph.

"Good news, Tony! Book your next flight back here tonight. I got a tryout for you."

"Thank you, God!" He blurted out loud, looking up at the sky through the sunroof. Momma looked over at Tony.

"What's going on, baby?" she excitedly asked.

"Coach Randolph got me a tryout with a team! He wants me be back in Arizona by the morning."

"YESSSS! THANK YOU LORD!" Momma shouted pumping one fist in the air with the other holding the steering wheel."

"YEAHHHH, BRA!" Chris said. Max and Chris reached over and grabbed Tony's shoulders and rubbing his head from the back seat.

"You know what time it is, lil' bra!" Max slapped Tony on the back of his head making his head jerk to the side.

"Aye, bra! Tighten up!" he said to Max with a slight smile on his face.

Momma grabbed Tony's hand and squeezed it. Tony stared at Momma as she drove holding her hand.

"I got this, Momma."

"No. God got this, baby. God got this," she replied.

On the way back home, Momma stopped and at the airport to drop off Tony. Pulling up to the terminal, Tony kissed Momma and jumped out to grab his bags from the trunk. Momma, Max and Chris got out to say their goodbyes.

"Alright, bra. Go out there and put on!" Chris said as he and Tony slapped hands and hugged. They held onto each other for another five seconds.

"Alright, nigga. Watch out!" Max pulled them apart.

"Give me some love too, bra," Max said, hugging his little brother. They all laughed. Tony walked over to Momma and squeezed her tight. As they rocked, he whispered in her ear.

"Momma I love you and I promise I'm gonna get you out of here. Whatever it takes. I'm all in."

"I love you, my baby." He leaned over, she kissed him on the cheek, and they all stood and watched as Tony walked in the airport.

"Come on, y'all. We gotta get to Quana!" Momma said as she ran around to the driver side of the car jumped in, and headed home.

Chapter Twenty-Seven

"We have now landed in Phoenix, Arizona. The weather here today is 106 degrees with clear skies. We hope you enjoyed your flight. Thank you for flying with Delta. Please come back soon."

Tony grabbed his ASU backpack from the overhead compartment and exited the plane. As he walked through the airport, he turned on his phone to call Coach Randolph to let him know he was back in town and ready for the tryout. He started dialing the number when his phone rang.

"You have a collect call from "Stew" an inmate in the Lorain correctional facility. To accept dial 0 and hold."

Tony was excited to hear from his brother for the first time. It was a bittersweet moment.

"What's up, bra?" Tony answered.

"What's up? How you feeling?" Stew asked.

"Mannn... it's hard. I just gotta get on the field. I'ma be good, bra," Tony said, walking through the airport.

"I know it's gonna be hard but hard times is what make us stronger, lil' bra," Stew said.

"I promise I'ma make sure I do what I gotta do to get you out of there," Tony said

"Don't worry about me, bra. Focus on you. If I have to do a hundred years for keeping y'all from gettin' hurt then, oh well. You just focus on you and your career. I love you, bra. I gotta get off this phone."

"I got you, bra. I love you. Call me back when they let you use the phone."

"Alright, bra. I love you too."

Back in Cleveland, Momma, Max, and Chris pulled up to Quana's house. The police were gone by the time they arrived. Momma pulled in Quana's driveway and they ran in the house. Quana lived down stairs in a white two-family house. Pierre moved in with her after he was released from doing a five-year sentence.

Momma, Max, and Chris walked into Quana's house and saw her on the couch crying.

"What happened, Quana?" Momma asked.

Max and Chris sat on the couch next to her as Momma stood over her.

"They came here looking for Max," Quana cried.

"Who?" Max asked surprisingly.

"They said something about you being involved with a homicide but when they detained Pierre, he hit one of the officers. They charged him with assault on an officer."

Max freaked out. "What? I ain't kill nobody! Is you forreal? They said my name, Quana?"

"Yes!" Quana said, wiping her face, rocking on the couch.

"Awww, you know what, bra?" Chris said looking at Max as an epiphany popped in his head.

Max looked at Chris.

"Remember we was sittin' on the porch that day and we heard the gunshots on the next street and Tony ran in the house?"

"Yop," Max said, shaking his head in deep thought.

"Jesus, Jesus, Jesus..." Momma repeated. She had her eyes shut tight looking at the ceiling, praying this wasn't true.

"Aww, naw. They ain't bouta say I did that! We out!" Max jumped off the couch and walked out the door.

"Where you going, bra?" Chris asked.

"To turn myself in so they can get my name out of this," Max said as he stormed out Quana's house. Chris and Momma followed Max out the door to the police station where Max turned himself in to clear his name. He told Momma not to tell Tony about this because he didn't want any more unnecessary stress on him. Max decided to hurry up and clear his name out of it and let Tony focus on his future in football.

Back in Arizona, Tony had no idea what was going on in Cleveland and Momma liked it that way because he could focus more on football than negative situations. She decided not to tell Tony what was going on with Max.

Tony walked into Coach Randolph's office to learn more about the tryouts that were on the table. "What's up, Coach?" Tony said smiling as he walked into his office.

Although Tony's spirit was really crushed on the inside, he tried not to let it show externally. He stayed in a positive mood around everybody. "How's my boy?" Coach Randolph replied.

"I'm blessed, Coach."

"Yes, you are," he said, resting his hand on Tony's shoulder.

"Here's the deal, Tony. I contacted nearly every team in the league. None of them are interested because there's a homicide involved with your name."

Tony stared into his eyes as he continued talking.

As Coach Randolph spoke, he saw and felt the intensity in his eyes and saw how hungry he looked. "But I reached out to some of my people in Canada.

They looked at your stats and highlight tape and they're interested in giving you a two-year contract."

"YESS!" Tony said, interrupting Coach Randolph. Although that's not what his dream was, he was excited to even get a shot on a team. Coach Randolph continued.

"If you go over there for two years and dominate and get your film up, I'm almost certain teams over here will start calling. Go over to Canada and make some noise," Coach Randolph demanded.

"Thanks, Coach. I'm goin' over there and going to work," Tony said.

"Yeah, so have your bags ready tomorrow. They're expecting you to be there in two days."

"It's personal," Tony said before he walked out coach of Coach Randolph's office.

When Tony arrived in Canada, he got his first phone call from Frank since he was sentenced to three years.

"W'sup, bra?" Frank said.

"What's up, bra? Why you ain't been calling?"

"They had us on redzone."

"What's that?" Tony asked.

"When they keep us locked in a cell all day with no phones or TV."

"Damn bra, I'm sorry, man. Y'all didn't have to take that deal. We could've beat this. We ain't do nothin!"

"I know but it is what is. Now we gotta do this time, so you just focus on football. What position Cincinnati got you playing?"

"Cincinnati took the deal off the table."

"What?" Frank said, pulling the phone back off his ear as he looked at the receiver, surprised from what he had just heard. Frank never knew that Cincinnati took the deal off the table. This was all news to him.

"Yeah but it's cool, bra. I'm in Canada now. I'm bouta start playing out here," Tony said.

"Okay, okay. Cool," Frank said.

"I'ma do two years here then hopefully they give me a shot in the league."

"Okay, just put that work in and stay in shape. Keep working, lil' bra. God gon take care of the rest," Frank said.

"You already know, bra."

Frank and Stew made sure they called and talked to Tony twice daily. They both knew about Max being convicted of a homicide and not to let Tony know about it.

After a few weeks passed, Tony eventually found out and he shocked his family after they saw how strong he stayed once he got the news. His faith in God overpowered any worries.

Tony took Uncle Reggie's advice and went into tunnel vision. He knew his brother was innocent and nobody had control but God. Tony's whole life was behind him.

From that day forward, he and Chris talked on the phone every day and they kept up each other's faith. Chris kept a big smile on his face. Nobody could ever tell if he was in a bad mood. Chris and Tony grew so close with Tony's siblings being incarcerated, their communication level went through the roof. Chris FaceTime'd Tony nearly every day and right before his first game he called.

"What's up, bra?" Chris said, displaying his big smile as Tony smiled back at him on the iPhone.

"What's up, Chris?" Tony said.

"I feel sorry for that running back coming up the middle," Chris said laughing as he continued. "All the stress built up in you, you're liable to kill somebody out there on that field." Chris stood at the gas station pumping gas into his Chevy Tahoe as he talked to Tony on the phone.

"I can't wait to get that feeling of being on the field, bra. You just don't know," Tony said.

"I can't wait. I'm 'bout to pull up to the house and watch the game," Chris said.

"Alright, bra. I'ma call you after the game," Tony said.

"Alright, I love you, bra. Go off on them boys out there."

"I love you, too. You already know, bra."

Tony strapped up in his first professional football game in Canada. He said a soft prayer as he sat on the bench in the locker room before the game.

"God, thank you so much for giving me this opportunity to do what I love. Please stay with me. Stay with Momma and all my family. God I know you're with us and I know this is just a test. God, just help us find the strength to fight through the rough times and keep faith. In your name, Amen."

Tony ran through the tunnel onto the field. The feeling he had as he ran was crazy. It felt as if everything that he and his family had been through was falling off his back. As he got closer and closer to the field, he left everything on the field.

He dominated the game that day and led the team in tackles and tackles for loss. His first game was an outstanding performance and he had many Canadian fans after just one performance.

After a year of hard work doing "three-a-days," and devastating news of his brother Max being found guilty of a crime he didn't commit, he kept his head held high and continued to strive to be the greatest he could be.

One day after practice, Tony was working overtime at the practice field when he got some of the best news he heard in a while: his brother Frank would possibly be getting released early after serving half of his time due to good behavior.

Frank and two other inmates Bear and Justin started a nonprofit organization inside the prison. After another judge had heard the story about Tony and his brothers, she decided to take over the case and bring Frank back to court.

Tony immediately called Momma when he got the news.

"Hello? Momma, please tell me this is true."

"Yesss, baby! Yes! God is sooo good!" Momma cried through the phone.

Tony put the phone down and pumped his fist. "Thank you, God!" He said softly. "I'm flying home. I gotta see my brother! I will leave the next day."

Momma couldn't say no. She knew how excited Tony would be to finally see his brother.

"Okay, baby but no clubbing and you're staying at home with me."

"Okay, Momma," Tony said as he hung up the phone to call Chris.

He called Chris' phone over and over to tell him the good news. Nobody was going to be more excited than Chris to find out Frank was being released early. "Why he ain't answering the phone?" Tony said to himself.

This was unusual. Chris always answered his phone unless he was asleep or extremely busy. Tony sent him a text.

"Call me, bra. Frank coming home." Tony knew he would respond to that text whether he was busy or not.

But Chris had been popping those pills again. Nothing too much, just enough that he didn't pay attention to the calls from Tony. Or to the road. He got himself into a small accident and bumped his head. Not feeling well, he decided to go home and go to sleep.

Tony woke up the next morning to Momma screaming in his ear.

"Chrisssss!" she cried.

"Huh, Momma? What's wrong?" Tony asked, half sleep wiping his eyes.

"Chris is dead, Tony," Momma cried.

"What?" Tony hollered as he sat up in his bed.

"Chris is dead! Chris is dead!"

Tony's entire body went completely numb. Tears uncontrollably rolled down his cheeks. Chris meant so much to Tony, his heart physically began to hurt when he heard the news. This was it for Tony. He felt like he reached his breaking point. His whole life had been ruined from one night, from one decision. He found out that one split second can ruin an entire life.

Chris had gone to sleep and just didn't wake up the next morning. Those pills were more than his body could take.

God gives everyone a certain amount of time to live. What a person does in the time He gives them is up to them.

God called Chris home and it was unexpected. He was only twenty-eight years old. Chris' death caught Tony off guard, it tore him apart, but somehow he found hope in everything he had been through. He continued to fight for a chance to play on the professional level.

Tony flew back to Cleveland when Frank went to court for an early release hearing. Momma sat in the courtroom with Tony and Quana. They all held hands waiting on Frank to walk through the doors. After an hour passed, the judge asked about Frank.

"Where is he?" the judge inquired.

"I don't know. I went back there and looked for him I can't find him," the bailiff responded.

Tony stood up in the courtroom. "Can I go back there to go get my brother?" he asked.

The judge laughed. "No, you may not."

Frank finally walked into the courtroom wearing shackles. The judge looked into Frank's eyes. "I heard about everything you and your family have been through and I want to tell you something: I respect you, and I don't want you to let this define you, young man," she said.

Frank dropped his head fighting back tears trying to gather himself before he spoke. Tony, Momma and Quana squeezed each other's hands with their eyes locked on Frank.

Frank held his head down thinking how much he and his family had been through and how much he had to deal with daily behind those penitentiary walls.

Tony stared at Frank with his head down.

He and Frank had been tight since they were babies. Tony could sense Frank's feelings and vice versa. Tony and Frank had a bond like Momma had with her baby sister. They also were still trying to cope with the loss of their close brother; not to mention Max and Stew who both were serving over twenty years. Frank slowly lifted his head up and looked into the judge's eyes.

"Your Honor," he said. He paused and looked back at his family sitting in the courtroom. They were all holding hands and looking at him stand at the podium in an orange County Jail jumpsuit.

"Thank you," he said, giving her a stern look in the eyes.

Frank was released later that day. Tony covered Naz's eyes with his hands as Frank walked through the door.

"You ready?" Tony said to Naz. He covered his face.

"For what?" Naz asked. He didn't have a clue his dad was coming home.

"1...2...3!" Tony said as he pulled his hand away from Naz's face. His eyes got wide as his jaw dropped with his hands on his head.

"DAD!" Naz ran and jumped into Frank's arms. The feeling was priceless. Tony hadn't seen any smiles around the family since draft day. Tony pulled Frank to the side to talk to him.

"Bra, it's only us left out here. We gotta do this for Momma, for the family, for our brothers. I don't want nothing to happen to you. I don't want you to leave me again, bra."

"I know. Bra. We gon' get through this, and we gon' get Max and Stew out of there."

"I'm leavin' back out tomorrow," Tony said.

"Okay, bra. Just keep working. Something gonna pop for you. Somebody gon' give you a shot on a team," Frank said before Tony cut him off.

"Bra, whatever happens it happens. I'ma keep working and trying my best to make it to get a tryout for a team. If it don't happen, then I'm going to move on, bra. Life is all about changes and if you don't know how to adapt to changes you'll end up wasting a lot of time."

"You right, bra. God got us and as long as we keep grinding and keep our faith in Him then it's inevitable for us to be great. It's just a matter of time before it all happens."

"I love you, bra. I'm bouta make it happen," Tony said as he put his hand out to give Frank some dap. They slapped hands, hugged and held each other for a long time. Momma looked at her boys hugging and cried as she displayed a smile.

Epilogue

No matter who you are or what you are, keep working. The harder you work, the more opportunities you'll have. Sometimes what you're looking for is right in front of your face. Keep going and you will succeed. The moment you stop or give up is when you lose.

Max is currently serving a 33-year sentence. He was railroaded by the system because of the reputation he had in the streets.

Stew is serving a 22-year sentence for protecting his family.

Momma is still keeping her faith in the Lord, working her job at the daycare, and praying to see her sons free.

Since Frank has been released, he has been fighting for appeals to get Max a chance at another trial and to get Stew a better deal.

As for Tony, he is still working out three times a day. He's running football youth camps, and giving all he can back to the people and City of East

Cleveland. And of course, he's still trying to play ball...

THE END

ABOUT THE AUTHOR

Surrounded by loud noises, arguing, fighting, dominos slamming against the cold hard table, that was what my life had become.

My name is Chris Johnson and I was sentenced to three years in prison for obstructing justice.

I was staying up 'til 4am most nights to dig deep inside and write about issues, both mentally and emotionally, that affected me and my family. 4th & Trenches is my journal.

Based around the things that really happened, and told from my point of view, it tells the story about my baby brother, Tony. I watched him dedicate his life, working hard day after day trying to turn his dream of becoming a pro football player into a reality.

My mom raised all of her children to be close, there was no way to tell Tony's story without including the most important aspect of it—his family. The journey in writing my first book has been like a movie, really. A rollercoaster ride of emotions ranging from laughter to anger to breaking down in tears. It hasn't been easy for me or for any one of us.

I hope this story will inspire someone to keep fighting, no matter what obstacles the devil throws at you. So enjoy and most importantly, learn how to fight through the trenches.

MOTIVATIONAL QUOTES

You take a loss, don't cry about it. Just embrace it, minor setback for a major comeback. That's my favorite.

-Kendrick Lamar

Count yo' blessings not yo' problems.

-Chris Johnson

Every day you should strive to learn something new and to be a better you.

-Abby L. Vandiver

You are your problem and your answer. When you show the work on yourself, your life will be your answer.

-Antonio Longino

WORDS OF ENCOURAGEMENT FROM EMORY JONES

Trust the process and give yourself a chance.
My Bet on Yourself really comes from we bet on everyone else so why not put self first.
We not supposed to be here, so we already won.
And there is way more wins out there living clean, than the streets.
Don't spread yourself thin. Find your land and ride it.
Everything happens for a reason. Good, bad and ugly.

-Emory Jones

Today, Tony is running football youth camps, and giving all he can back to the people and City of East Cleveland.